The Clar

For Ivy, with love
from Greta.

The Clary Ghost

Greta McDonough

The Pentland Press Limited
Edinburgh • Cambridge • Durham • USA

First published in 1998 by
The Pentland Press Ltd.
1 Hutton Close
South Church
Bishop Auckland
Durham

British Library Cataloguing in Publication Data.
A Catalogue record for this book is available
from the British Library.

ISBN 1 85821 607 9

Typeset by CBS, Felixstowe, Suffolk
Printed and bound by Antony Rowe Ltd., Chippenham

For the girls of the McDonasty and
the shade of Pangur Dhu.

CONTENTS

CONTENTS

For the Lord shall comfort Zion: he will comfort all her waste places; and he will make her wilderness like Eden, and her desert like the garden of the Lord; joy and gladness shall be found therein, thanksgiving and the voice of melody.

Isaiah 51:3

Hours fly
Flowers die
New days
New ways
Pass by
Love stays

Source unknown

CHAPTER ONE

SUDDEN SUNDAY

D earest Daisy,

I must write to you though it will be years if ever before you read this letter. A few hours ago I didn't know of your existence. And now, here I am, a full-blown grandmother suffering only from shock after getting that call from your father in Port Elizabeth.

Fancy your mother keeping it a secret all these months! I know why she did; she has had so many gynaecological problems and she didn't want to raise any hopes in vain. But I could have been knitting a lacy shawl for you or collecting silver spoons . . .

Still, I always did love surprises and this must be the best of my life. I had had a very quiet Sunday until then, lighting the fire, arranging fresh flowers – pink japonica and creamy winter clematis – and thinking about putting the lunch in the oven. Then your father rang. I was a bit puzzled by this, as he knows I prefer letters and my thrifty soul shrinks at the cost of even a few minutes talk with South Africa. Then he told me about you, and you could have knocked me down with a feather. In fact, I almost thought it was some belated April Fool except that I knew he would not do that to me. He was a bit shaken after being present at your birth, and described how you blinked when confronted with the light for the first time. I was too surprised to make any sensible comments. At one point I heard myself asking, 'And when can she come and stay with me by herself?'

Then it was time to ring off, and I was left to come to terms with an idea that most women have several months to get used to. I was like someone who has just fallen in love, conscious only of the beloved regardless of barriers or future difficulties.

I wanted first of all to talk about you. Most of the people I rang were grandparents already – it would have seemed like boasting to tell some of the others at that point.

Pamela's response was the most profound, a welcome to a new and dear person. It added a new dimension to my life, she said. This expresses it perfectly. I walked round the garden in my excitement, seeing it through the eyes of the small child who, God willing, will run there. I was glad the oriental poppy was beginning to thrive. I still remember encountering its huge scarlet flowers in my grandmother's garden. And I was glad that I had the big old fashioned lavender bushes, grown from cuttings from that same garden.

I thought that the thorns and nettles would do you no harm, teaching you the importance of regarding warning signs. Pan you would probably chase, but one or two attempts to hold him would soon place him in the prickly category. I dreamed of you coming to stay, first with your parents and then, when you became really at home with me, alone. Oh, darling, how I wish you lived just down the lane, so that you could start dropping in on me in your pram immediately.

I picture myself singing the old nursery rhymes to you as my mother did to me. She was very fond of songs like 'What shall we have for dinner, Mrs Bond?' and 'Oh, No John'. I must look them up because in my memory a lot of them have one or two lines missing.

Do you know that your coming has fulfilled one of my life's three ambitions? I shall keep the other two secret as they might still come true in such an astounding fashion as this one.

I have wired your mother some flowers, but how I wish I could send her a posy such as my mother remembered all her life receiving after the birth of one of her May children. It consisted simply of tight blue grape hyacinths surrounded by a plethora of forget-me-nots. I think florists have lost the confidence to despatch such simple posies today.

Tomorrow I am going to the shops to look for the contents of a special parcel. One of the items will be a beautiful wooden teether I was looking at the other day and regretting that I had no baby to buy it for. It's too late for a shawl, your mother will already have got one, but I shall get restrung some tiny coral beads which look made for a little girl's first necklace.

I can honestly say I have never regretted not having a daughter, probably because I doubt my capacity to rear one well. I have not been a great success as a woman. But a grand-daughter is a different matter. Your mother with all her feminine gifts will raise you admirably while I revel in the arrival of a girl in the family.

In fairy stories when a baby is born there is often a wicked fairy who imposes a spell on her and then the fairy godmother who appears in the nick of time to redress things. I have been thinking what gift I would bestow on you if I were your fairy godmother.

As a child of the Sabbath day you should already be destined to be blithe and bonny and good and gay in the old sense of the word. If you weren't destined to be bonny I don't think I would bestow beauty. I remember a stunning German au pair girl with dark red hair and milky skin, child of divorced parents, who assured me that beauty was more trouble than it was worth. And I can count on the fingers of one hand the people I have met who were beautiful and not vain.

Similarly with intelligence. I wouldn't want to bestow on you the gift of great intelligence: it carries too much responsibility. Intelligence increases a person's ability to do damage in this world, unless it is balanced by great humility.

What I would like to give you is the gift of appreciativeness. Perhaps it is better called the spirit of delight.

One of my friends has it. It is something she inherited or learned from her mother and I like to think that after sharing a flat with her a little of it has rubbed off on me.

Everything nice that happens to her, every gift she gets, she exclaims about, and knowing this you find yourself conspiring to give her treats just for the pleasure of witnessing her pleasure. People, even those she meets casually, metaphorically get out their best china for her and the result is that her life is much better than those of people who begrudge any praise or enthusiasm. Even if someone fails to deliver something promised: 'Well, we shan't have to thank him for it,' is her reaction. Some call it serendipity – the art of making happy discoveries – and if I could I would bestow it on you.

St Teresa of Avila must have had it for she wrote somewhere that she was so easily pleased that she could be bought with a sardine. Mark Twain must have been thinking of it when he said he could live for a month on a good compliment. For appreciativeness is a subtle form of creativity. Appreciative people are encouragers (Dr Johnson's word), enabling others to give of their best. Appreciativeness is neither a carrot nor a stick. It is a pat on the side or a stroke of the muzzle which is much more effective in persuading a well kept donkey to give of its best.

If we only treasured what we had, we would be less likely to demand more, thus solving many of the world's problems at one stroke. And much of the work which is now done half-heartedly would be tackled with enthusiasm at the prospect of a little appreciation.

And now with all these things running in my head I must get back to my ordinary Sunday activities. Tonight I plan to write to your other grandparents who are there on the spot and so missed the experience of surprise and wonder that your birth has brought me. By the time they get my letter they will no doubt have met you, and perhaps I shall get a letter in return giving me details which your father won't think to mention.

CHAPTER TWO

DANCE OF LIFE

April. Until now it has been my least favourite month. I have had to revise my attitude in the light of your arrival. It is now a very special month because it is yours.

I didn't like April because (whisper it) I don't much enjoy the English spring. Paradoxically, being born below the Equator you are both an April and an autumn child. I love autumn and send you the American Indian blessing: may you live a hundred autumns.

How will you react, I wonder, to an English April? Four seasons in one month. Four seasons in one day sometimes; it goads repeatedly with cold and light producing growth in the young and healthy but death in the old and sick. I would no more want to prolong it than to prolong childbirth. No wonder the country folk looked forward to May Day: 'March will search you, April will try, May will tell you whether you'll live or die.'

April sees the courtship of the sun and rain. This morning it has rained, and the drops on my bedroom window combine with those on the trees, green and silver, to make a pointillist picture and make me feel like a whale swimming in a sea of plankton. Pan leaps in, his black coat sparkling, the drops coalescing to wet my hand when I stroke him.

A bluetit like a tiny whale has been harvesting the plankton outside my window these last few days. Invisible to me, they are generated by the noisette Mme Alfred Carrière which climbs underneath and beside the panes, its young shoots interspersed with the grape-like buds of the *Clematis macropetalla*. The tit lands on the rose, flies up to tap the window in short bursts and after a harvest of upwards of a dozen taps returns to its box next door. Returning every three minutes or so, it must collect well over a thousand mites a day.

The tit's sorties remind me of some strange dance. In this climate, April leads us all a dance. Its music gets more and more compelling, a Highland fling or a tarantella until the warmth arrives and the frenzy subsides into the gavotte of May.

Finn McCool, the Irish hero, was once asked, 'What is the best music of all?' He replied, 'The best music of all is the music of what happens.' This puzzled me until I realised that he must have been talking about the music of the dance. Life is like a dance. The music is there and we have to follow it as best we can, with good grace or bad, learning the steps as we go along. We can't always get them right but we can try, and often the same passage will come round again, failure, joy, bereavement, success, giving us a chance to do it better each time. Work gives the dance its rhythm, so that it is not just a mêlée.

Frequently recurring passages are what we call routine. When I was a child I hated routine, associating it with school. Life in newspapers, with all its irregularity, was balm after that, but even newspapers have their routines, police calls, magistrates' courts, deadlines and weekly columns. I have come to appreciate routine, the routine of a small child's day, of caring for animals, of being helpless in hospital or of a planned week. Pushkin called it the next thing to happiness, and often it is the field in which happiness flourishes. Repetition takes the strain out of things and makes novelty and surprise the more delightful.

Even the spaces in a dance count – they are the rests and it is the absence of them which is the frightening thing about the Dance of Death in the *Rite of Spring*. When, as children, we had tea at my grandmother's and ate rather too quickly we were taught when we were asked what we would like next to say, 'A pause, please.' Life is full of necessary pauses, night, winter, sickness, pregnancy. Even bread and pastry making need their pauses if the result is to be satisfactory.

Another important factor in the dance of life is tempo. So often when we are young we try too hard and do things too fast. Learning to swim and to ride a bicycle are examples of this. The right tempo makes things much easier. When I was a child I could never whip egg white until I realised that in my anxiety I was whipping too fast and giving no time for the air to be folded in.

But besides being a dance April in Norfolk is primrose scented. Is there any scent in Africa like that of freshly picked primroses? Primrosing was an important event of my childhood, before the countryside was in retreat and picking wild flowers became an offence. In the sun near the summerhouse you can get a small taste of it, complete with the cold and the wet and the prickling of brambles which are usually part of it. Someone described the hairy pink stems which stretch then break when pulled as darning wool stems. But what child nowadays knows about darning wool?

The scent of primroses is a reminder too that in April I celebrate the anniversary of my coming to this house. The purple primroses inside the front bank were the first flowers that I picked here. On moving day, my neighbour handed through the hedge a nosegay from her garden which included primulas. How flowers can lubricate human relations. They were strained though within twenty-four hours when Pan demolished a treasured blackbird's nest in the same hedge, despite your father's attempts to protect it. I'm glad to say the blackbirds nested again in a safer place.

I hope Pan won't do the same to the nest the long tailed tits have built in the escallonia. They have only just finished feathering it. I feel as I did when as a child I was given something very fragile to hold or carry, a mixture of pride and fear. It is a source of pride when a creature trusts you enough to nest near you. If you came to visit me today, we would have to give the escallonia a wide berth as well as the hedge near the compost heap where I suspect the robins have been building.

Instead I must introduce you to the three hens, Patty and Kitty and Lottie who live in an ark in the orchard. Maran bantams, chocolate coloured with silver necks, I thought them a little dull when I first saw them. But I don't keep them for their looks but for their eggs, small, deep brown, and sometimes speckled, which I would not exchange for any others.

Then you must see the heirloom plant which is at its best now, its spikes of wide eyed blue flowers springing from a desolation of brown leaves. Its real name is *Omphalodes cappodocica* but I call it the heirloom plant because I got it from a cousin who got it from an aunt who got it from a brother.

You should like your name plants, the double daisies; I had a hen and chickens daisy once but it got lost

In the frame are two bullace seedlings sprung from stones I planted hopefully in the autumn. In the kitchen garden the shallots and broad beans are looking trim. I can see why someone said that people having nervous breakdowns should sit in kitchen gardens. They have that air of firm tenderness so comforting in the best hospitals.

Apart from primroses and daffodils, spring flowers are still shy in this cold spot but we could walk round the garden savouring scents between finger and thumb. I was a thumb sucker when young and know the taste of most plants in the garden through handling them – I well remember the acrid taste of pot marigolds. I like to put aromatic flowers on all corners and many of the edges so that one brushes against them. You don't even need to touch the sweetbriar – its new leaves scent the air powerfully. In the front garden we can find marjoram, lemon balm and several sages as well as the pungent geranium, *macrorrhyzum*. Near the house are the rosemaries, lavenders and artemisias. You'd better not touch the rue; it has the bitterest smell I know.

Round the back of the house are the myrtle, the bay, and the eucalyptus which has shot up way above me in only a few years. We shall have to wait some time yet for the mints and the verbena to sprout much. Madame Alfred's leaves smell faintly of roses when they are full grown but I doubt if we should perceive it with our smelly fingers. And we must not interrupt the window-cleaner tit.

While we are outside we must keep a sharp lookout for swallows. I haven't yet seen the first. In my garden book which goes back fifteen years the earliest day for the first swallow is 18th April. Twice it came on the 26th, once on the 28th and once on the 29th. The first cuckoos were heard on the 22nd and the 28th. The swifts don't usually arrive till May nor does the mulberry unfold its leaves before then though one year I recorded mulberry buds breaking on 30th April.

I started my garden book in a 1937 Galeries Lafayette diary found in a junk shop and afterwards copied the entries into a more suitable page-a-day diary. I didn't know then that I was in august company. Gilbert White started his *Garden Kalendar* in 1751 on quarto sheets of writing paper which were afterwards stitched together. His *Naturalist's Journal* which succeeded it in

1768 was kept in notebooks printed in columns. It still included occasional garden notes, but also the observations which he used for his *Natural History of Selborne*. Some of the entries read like poems.

At least the swallows won't be strangers to you when you come to England. Gilbert White thought they and the martins hibernated here and instigated searches for them but could never find them. We know that they go to Africa in pursuit of summer, but they return, the males at least, to the very nests and sheds where they were hatched. They pair during their flight back and the females accompany the males to their homes in true patriarchal fashion.

When we come in, while I get the lunch, cheese pudding followed by rhubarb and banana, you might like to wipe the leaves of the money plant for me. I have some stale milk and a bit of worn handkerchief. I used to love such laborious jobs when I was a child. If you find it dull, I will tell you the story of how when this money plant was small and part of a garden of mixed succulents I picked it up to water it and saw a jewel-like eye gazing at me. I thought I was imagining things but looked closer and found it belonged to a large toad crouched there among the succulents. The bowl garden had been outside a day or two before to get the spring rain and the toad must have arrived then and crouched motionless while I carried it back to the living room. I like toads but they do have a power to startle out of all proportion to their size. I have dug them up in the compost heap and been horrified to see what looked like a clod turn into a living creature.

Then it will be time for our rests. You may not have one at home, but at the Dacha they're the order of the day. You needn't lie with the curtains drawn but may choose one of the books I have kept from my childhood – Alex took his away with him.

I wish I had a *Milly-Molly-Mandy* book to give you for your rest, because this afternoon I thought we might turn out the summerhouse and this is the sort of thing Milly-Molly-Mandy did. Alas, I have never seen her since my childhood and I expect she and Little Friend Susan have been consigned to oblivion, along with Little Black Sambo, who was as popular then as Peter Rabbit. No reprinting for them. We will put on scarves and overalls – you can wear one of my old shirts – and carry all the contents of the summerhouse on to the grass to the perturbation of Pan who dreads any sign of another move. Then we can take up the matting and sweep out. I wish houses were as easy to clean. I wish, too, I had a little broom for you like the one I had when I was small. It came at a Valentine party at a big house when the doorbell kept ringing and when you answered it there was a parcel there on a string which twitched away unless you snatched it up quickly . . .

We're sure to find all sorts of treasures, just as I do when dismantling the compost heap: a missing teaspoon, a dead butterfly, a scarf lost since last summer. One day I hope to furnish it with a set of dolls' chairs and a dolls' teaset like the one I had when I was a child. I can picture it clearly, blue rims and yellow centres with a few red flowers, undoubtedly Japanese. Such as survive are collectors' pieces now.

I've already got, to preside over the dolls' teaparty, a grandmother doll, rescued from the charity shop where she was not appreciated. American made, of rag, she has a patchwork bonnet and dress, white lace edged apron and petticoat and a pair of button boots. Her eyes peer over spectacles. We must find a good name for her. What do you think of Babushka?

When the summerhouse is straight again, we'll have tea in it if it's warm enough with Babushka sitting in a chair and Pan, reassured, drinking milk out of a saucer.

CHAPTER THREE

FLOWERS BY POST

The birds had been forecasting rain for days and yesterday it came, a steady downpour. Today the trees seem twice as green; even the laggard ash is shooting and the rowan displays a wealth of silvery flower buds.

It gets light so early now that when I draw back the curtains Pan is often perched on the back of the seat waiting to leap in. One of the hens may be announcing the arrival of an egg and the cuckoo also advertises its presence. Relief at welcoming its return is compounded these days with guilt about the scene to which we welcome it.

Under the window, hairy seedheads are forming in the purple clematis and I can hear a bumble bee teasing one of the remaining flowers. The rose leaves are translucent in the sun, and every now and then a small bird flies across my view, its wings translucent too. A wood pigeon flew up almost vertically on to the roof above giving a momentary vision of fan-like wing feathers and tail, inspiration for paintings of angels' wings. Most other birds have disappeared behind the veil of green leaving behind only their voices.

I love these white mornings. I love all mornings nowadays. It's like being a child again. Gone are the apprehensions of school and working life, the day is no longer mortgaged and the morning is my own. At this time of year when it is fine I can breakfast in bed sitting in the sunshine. This is the first house – the first bedroom – I have had which gets the morning sun.

For those of us who did not enjoy our schooldays, and Wordsworth spoke for us, it takes a long time to erase the effects of that long sentence. Someone said that noise and haste were the Devil's two minions. That's how I remember school: noise and haste. It didn't help that my generation of girls was taught by 'surplus women', those made single by the First World War. Life must have been empty for many of them. A friend remembers a maths teacher so irascible that in one exam the highest mark she awarded was minus nine.

Compulsory education has its roots in the night schools organised by philanthropists for the child victims of the industrial revolution. Anthropology tells us that true education is the concern of parents and grandparents. Now this responsibility and privilege has been lost to schools, television and computer games.

Things were different in Ladakh, Little Thibet, that least industrial of countries before it was opened to Western exploitation. Helena Norberg-Hodge in her book *Ancient Futures* describes life there in the absence of schools.

> Children are never segregated into peer groups; they grow up surrounded by people of all ages from young babies to great grandparents. They grow up as part of a whole chain of relationships, a chain of giving and taking.

Old people participated in all spheres of life, they were important members of the community until the day they died. In a life which had no hurry, it did not matter if they worked more slowly. One of the reasons why they remained alive and involved was their constant contact with the young. 'The relationship between grandparent and child is different from that between parent and child. The very oldest and the very youngest form a special bond; they are often best friends.'

Ladakhis grew up non-competitive and with a simple happiness which it took years to convince the author – she spent six months of the year in Ladakh for many years – was not put on. One of the reasons was the limited nature of communication.

> The incredible vitality and joy that I experienced in the villages was almost certainly connected to the fact that the excitement in life was here and now with you and in you. People did not feel that they were on the periphery; the centre was where they were.

Very little of my education except the negative part happened at school. My education of the mind took place over my parents' dining table, through the contents of my father's bookcases and in the reporters' rooms of various newspapers where the apprenticeship system still prevailed. You learned your trade from someone who had learned his trade from someone who had learned his trade . . . Here I emerged from the distrust and competition of my schooldays into a world of respect and mutual aid.

My education of the hand was the gift of many individuals including the aunt who taught me scotch darning, the landlord who showed me the best way to tie a parcel, Robert who on leave from National Service taught me the meaning of spit and polish, a lady overheard on a bus who gave me the secret of invisible mending and Dermot who not before time told me how to open a corned beef tin without cutting myself (swathe the vulnerable hand in a cloth). I remember them all with gratitude when I use these skills. Few of them have I passed on:

people don't seem to want them these days.

My education of the heart began in my twenties when I was admitted to a mental hospital with acute depression. I learned that under all their differences people have many bonds. Adversity is often needed to reveal this.

Yesterday I picked bluebells and cow parsley from the far bank, remembering the nuns who use cow parsley in their chapel, mixing wild and garden flowers – no apartheid there. This is an area renowned for bluebells. Sheets of them grow in the vestigial oak woods filling them with that incomparable scent. I didn't know until the other day that bluebells are essentially a British flower. They stray on to the Continent but not in such abundance.

I'm told cow parsley is on sale these days in the streets of London, a measure of nostalgia for the countryside.

The garden now is full of forget-me-nots and honesty flowering in unexpected places. The compost is never free of their seeds and I am not strong-minded enough to keep them where they belong. When we walk round the garden we will take the kitchen scissors and you shall pick some of the lilies of the valley which are spreading nicely in the hermaphrodite border. They are the complement of the bluebells, more common on the Continent than here. My mother remembered them in the woods of Russia, a small plenty in the large waste of famine.

Mary was telling me that as a child she used to pick lilies of the valley in a wood and bunch them to be sent by post to an aunt who had a greengrocer's shop in London. One of the things I planned to do when I was grown up was to send people flowers by post. I had visions of their surprise on opening a dull brown paper parcel to find bunches of cold snowdrops, scented violets or dewy primroses. But I have never done it.

Berthe Morisot sent a parcel of roses to the poet Mallarmé at his country home in 1888 when she was staying at Nice. She must have read his letter to her husband Eugène Manet the previous summer when he wrote: 'I lack flowers and I fancy that your eyes are spared this suffering, the worst of all privations. At times I would give the centuries of a tree for a few pinks.'

Mallarmé warmly acknowledged the roses and Berthe wrote back: 'For my faded flowers you have rewarded me by a very kind and charming letter. I shall send you more, this time from my garden; this is a method of correspondence customary in this region and quite within my means. In return you will send me your charming prose.'

Lilies of the valley feature in the letters of a Latvian woman I have been reading, whose husband every year presented her with a pot on her birthday, March 19th. Despite two World Wars and German and Russian occupations she recorded in the year of her death the sixty fourth pot in succession, the first having been received the year of her engagement.

What constancy! What might I not have done if I had been granted a life of such stability? Experience has taught me though that other people's paradises are for me often fools' ones. By the time the tenth pot came along I would probably gladly have foregone it for a surprise, anything, anything other than lilies of the valley. A white hydrangea which arrived for my birthday last year and is now planted out in the courtyard brought with it that delight of the unexpected.

But I am not unprejudiced about lilies of the valley. Years ago, as a young reporter, I was carrying my week's rations in a holdall with my clothes and a bottle of lily of the valley scent. It leaked, and fat is used as a solvent to extract perfumes. After eating lily of the valley butter for a week I can't feel quite the same about the flowers.

What shall we do before lunch? Well, if it's fine there are seedlings to be planted out and others to be thinned, a painful job which makes me think of Bangladesh. I have found some tiny hellebore seedlings under their parents in a crack between the paving stones and your fingers with the help of a kitchen fork will be fine for the job of planting them in pots. I want to cut back the hellebores and other plants; you can be truck man and cart the proceeds to the compost heap. Then, if there's time you can help me rescue some of the wild cherry seedlings from under the fairy apple tree where the birds have sown them. Tree roots go down very quickly – I suppose it's their way of seizing the chance of life. When I planted out the two bullace seedlings their roots were already circling the bottoms of the pots.

In the afternoon I thought we might do some canvas work. I have one of my cross stitch texts to finish and you might like to try your hand at cross stitch too. I have a book of little designs of flowers and animals which you could copy. Or we might take down the sampler with its two stripey cats and you could do a version all in black like Pan.

I was going to make a sampler of our last house but I never got round to it. I nearly bought one the other day because it was dated the year of my birth, 1930, and because I liked its message:

> Life is mostly froth and bubble
> Two things stand like stone
> Kindness in another's trouble
> Courage in your own.

It was too big and too dear so I memorised the words instead.

CHAPTER FOUR

SUMMER'S BEACONS

June

Yet another fine morning. We are still waiting for the monsoon. After weeks of dry weather I can hardly bear to look at the garden.

How dominated I am by the weather. Is it a particularly feminine trait? Karen Blixen, writing of the coming parting with her African farm, wrote: 'Till then I had been a part of it, and the drought had been to me like a fever and the flowering of the plain like a new frock.' Exactly, though she doesn't include the wonderful sense of relief that comes with a good rain. When it rains in the night I sleep extra deeply.

Rahel, whose salon was a focus of German life for twenty years in and after the Napoleonic occupation, often headed her letters with the weather as well as the date. 'Nothing is so important to me, so real, as weather,' she wrote in 1830. 'I am convinced that one day it will become a science and we shall then be able to compound weather as we do medicine.'

I wish I could draw. I would draw a picture called June Morning. In it I would put, framed in the window, the tossing trees, the glimpses of sky with white clouds and at the bottom the shoots of Mme Alfred with, in the right hand corner, one full blown pale pink rose.

Below the window on the sunlit cream counterpane I would draw Pan washing himself, his fur more brown than black at this time of year, the light glancing silver through his guard hairs and glowing pink through one ear. I could not possibly draw the light reflected on the walls from the moving leaves of the trees, flickering as the river light used to flicker on the ceiling of the house where your father was born.

Mme Alfred's first flowers coincide with the arrival of the wild roses. I marvel every year that hardly have I seen the first wild rose than they are all over every hedge, signalling the invasion of summer more instantly than any beacons.

> Very old are the woods;
> And the buds that break
> Out of the briar's boughs,
> When March winds break
> So old with their beauty are
> Oh, no man knows
> Through what wild centuries
> Roves back the rose.

We don't need to avoid the escallonia any more when we walk round the garden. The tits' nest is empty. The garden seems empty too without the lilting flight of those sparrow-coloured charmers. If I lift you up you can peer at and touch the beautiful deep nest made of silvery lichen and moss which made the old countrymen think of boiled puddings.

The tale of the long-tailed tits was very nearly a short one. I came round the corner one day to find Pan clutching a bird which looked surprisingly tiny apart from the tail. How he caught it I don't know as I have never seen one on the ground. It was dishevelled and stunned and sat for a time on a branch after I rescued it and took Pan indoors. Then it disappeared and I had hours of anxiety before I saw the birds had resumed their feeding dance.

Luckily Pan was indoors asleep on May 21st, St Godric's Day, when I found on the gravel another dishevelled tit, short tailed this time, and realised that the family had flown. There was no response when the baby uttered its characteristic tsui-tsui-tsui so I picked it up and gave it rose shoots with greenfly. Some time later, a tit was back in the escallonia so I hastily returned Godric (or Godrica). After some comings and goings the family disappeared, all of them this time.

In some parts of the country long tailed tits are known as ragamuffins. They seem so elegant to me that I can't believe the name is based on their appearance. A group of them together in a tree, though, behave like ragamuffins, chattering and calling. When I hear an excitement of them now I shall wonder if Godric is among them.

That grey cat who greets us in the garden is Pan, though you may not recognise him in his summer livery. He powders as assiduously as any eighteenth century gentleman these dry days, bathing in the dust pans in the lane which were once puddles.

After you have visited the hens and looked in the nest boxes for any eggs you must inspect the garden – the oriental poppy is at its best and the everlasting pea parades its magenta peacocks. I am longing to see your face when I show you the *Hieracium aurantiacum* for the first time and tell you its common name: fox and cubs. So far only the vixens have their eyes open.

I must do some watering, and you can help me. First we must remember the struggling shrubs in out of the way places like the rubus with shoots like silver claws planted two Christmases ago, the *Celastrus scandens* on the bank and the bamboo newly moved next to the pepper-pot toolshed.

Then there is the kitchen garden. The sweet peas planted

between the new raspberry canes and the peas between the new currants are only just coming up. They wouldn't have survived this year without watering. The beans between the gooseberries are only just showing too and they are the second planting. That small watering can with the rose will suit you nicely, so you can water the newly planted lettuces in the frame, the carnations which should be much bigger and the nasturtiums still only tiny after two months of cold and drought.

The seedlings in the big clay pots are mignonette, sown there so that I can bring them indoors when they are flowering. No-one seems to grow mignonette these days, probably because its main beauty is its scent. The Victorians appreciated it: they grew it in their greenhouses and kept it flowering all through the winter. (Rosa Luxemburg, on a speaking tour of Poland in June 1898, wrote to her lover that she had been given 'a lovely bunch of roses and mignonette'.) It was probably my father who introduced me to it. He used to boast of being a Victorian, though he was only five when the Old Queen died.

I hope while we are out in the garden we shall have the peace and quiet that belong to a fine morning and not be troubled by those serpents in my Garden of Eden, the military planes. At times I feel like shaking my fist at the dashing pilots who defile our skies with noise and fumes. How I envy Betsey Trotwood who had only donkeys to contend with.

We can have lunch in the summerhouse – or right outside if the weather is fine enough. I've got a crab landed yesterday by a boat called the *Justifier*. I'll show you one day where it is beached, not three miles from here as the crow flies.

Then it will be time for our rests. I came across a book on my shelves this week which might interest you, for its pictures if not its text. Called *Prayers from the Ark*, it contains poems written by a young French girl, Carmen Bernos de Gasztold, and put into the mouths of birds and animals and insects . . . It never fails to move me, but I would love to get it in the original French because, as someone said, the only thing that gets lost in the translation of poetry is the poetry.

Carmen de Gasztold suffered from mental illness and recovered in the shadow of the great Benedictine abbey at Limon-par-Igny, south of Paris. She then made her home there. In difficult times, I have envied her such a therapeutic environment.

Prayers from the Ark was not written in my childhood but was sent to your father by his Great Aunt Vi. I wish you could have met my mother's sister, Vi, the most cosmopolitan of my relatives. After a delicate childhood, and three years spent at home with her widowed father instead of studying medicine as she would have liked, she married her sister's brother-in-law who was in the Colonial Service and went with him to live in Malaya. Well I remember the joy with which her distinctively written letters with the Malayan stamps were received by my mother.

When we get up you can help me with some weeding. And I must see that if you are not already equipped with a hat you wear one of mine as the sun begins to be threatening after midday. I discovered only recently how much better the world is for me when seen from under a big hat. Sensitivity to light is an oppressive thing. My mother had the right idea when she went to a theatrical costumier's and bought sunbonnets for Judith and me as children. She had probably seen them worn in the Russian countryside.

This garden is very weedy by most standards. That's because I don't look on weeds as pests but as friends, not to be pulled up unless absolutely necessary. Like Thoreau, I am the attorney of the indigenous plants. Weeds, and the shower of leaves in autumn, are the wealth of the earth, the year's dividends or its capital gains. They are also the world's armour, protection against erosion by wind or water. I am reading a book by Wendell Berry, who among other things is a Kentucky farmer, in which he describes walking on yellow slopes where the missing topsoil would have reached up to his knees or even to his shoulders. In a hundred years of theft farming fifty or sixty thousand years' stock of fertility has been destroyed.

While we are pulling up the weeds, Daisy, attended by the intrepid blackbird, I will teach you their names as I learned them before I can remember. Shepherd's purse, with its tiny heart-shaped pods, groundsel, chickweed, whose name you will understand if you offer a bit to the hens, speedwell with its wide blue eyes. Some I can hardly bear to pull up even if they are in the wrong place: scarlet pimpernel, which closes in dull weather, heartsease which brings me back full circle to the first garden I ever knew, and self-heal, new to me with this garden. There are two saints' plants, St John's Wort and Herb Bennet. Red dead nettles I try to leave wherever I find them, as a lifeline for the bees in spring. So too are the dandelions, though I have to attack them in special hunts, my weapon an old knife. I know you'll be on their side, admiring their gorgeous golden scuts and sowing dozens with a few puffs when the clocks form.

One day, perhaps, you can help me compile a flora of this garden as Gilbert White did for Selborne. It should be quite extensive, as the ground has not been so long in cultivation as my other gardens. I never turn up oyster shells or bottles as I did on the quay, or old horseshoes as I did in town. Because of the woodland at the back there are plants like wood sage and ground ivy, which White called Gill go by Ground. This year I discovered wild arum growing in the hedge. There is lots of white bryony, and also black bryony which stumped me at first. Both are very poisonous though the first is related to the gourd and the second to the yam.

Weeds feature in the advice given to a friend by her mother just before her marriage. 'If you feel down,' she said, 'go into the garden and pull a few weeds.'

Knowing flowers and living with them has helped me to understand what the Buddhists mean by inner nature, the essence of each living thing. Like the soil, inner nature in both flowers and man is being deeply eroded. Any flower catalogue will show you how the flower breeders are doing their best to deny the flowers their natures. It's difficult to mistake a wild daffodil for a wild rose, a tulip for a peony, but by the time the breeders have finished with them their deepest features, the essential character which makes a larkspur not a columbine, a daisy not a bluebell, have been largely destroyed. Looking at modern Michaelmas daisies it is difficult to recognise the starwort which first arrived in Britain.

Cherish your inner nature, Daisy, no matter what pressure is put on you by parents, teachers or peer group to be like everyone else. Be yourself. The Hasidic rabbi Zusya was asked on his deathbed what he thought the Kingdom of God would be like. 'I don't know,' he replied. 'But one thing I do know. When I get there I am not going to be asked, "Why weren't you Moses? Why weren't you David?" I am going to be asked, "Why weren't you Zusya? Why weren't you fully you?"'

CHAPTER FIVE

TOUTE BONNE

July

What a beautiful still rainy morning. The rose leaves are pricked round with tiny drops and from my bed I can hear the water butt filling. The loveliest sound after drought is the sound of running water. The great Islamic psychiatrists used the sound of dripping water as well as music and hypnosis in their treatment of patients.

You'll need your boots if you come today. You'll get soaked visiting the hens but I don't suppose that will deter you. Every time I have to feed them in the wet I regret the disappearance of pattens.

The herby, sagey smell of the front garden is interrupted by a cool wet one but it will soon be back. The hum of bees, which is the soundtrack of the flower garden this month, is interrupted too but only briefly. Once the rain has stopped, the wetness of the flowers will not put them off. The garden is full of bee plants, because to me, bees, like a cat, are an essential part of a garden. I love to watch one crawling delicately up a foxglove flower and reversing out again, or dangling like a trapeze artist on a fuchsia bell. One of the reasons why I like the species brambles is their attraction for bees.

The anchusas, the intense blue of which always excites comment, are going over, but the claries are at their best. They puzzle most people, as they are rarely seen. They puzzled me too when I first saw them, but it was love at first sight, and before I even knew their name I had found my first seedling at a charity plant sale. From that and one I bought at a nursery they are all descended. They glow on fine summer evenings as stately as foxgloves with the light of the setting sun shining through their papery mauve bracts.

This big clary, called by the French 'Toute Bonne' and the English 'Cleareye', is well known to the herbalists. The sticky mucilage which the seeds produce in water was used for eye lotions. Aromatherapists use clary oil to restore nervous energy and relieve the effect of outside pressures. Its effect is described as exhilarating and euphoric. I put a drop or two in my bath water. The herb is also an ingredient in the best eau de colognes and the Germans know it as Muscatel sage because of its use in flavouring wines.

One of the eryngiums is known as Miss Willmott's Ghost, thanks to that lady's habit of scattering the seed in her friends' gardens. I have given away so much clary in the form of seeds and seedlings that if my ghost walks it will be in the shape of these bee-loved aromatic spikes, like nettles which have suffered a sea change.

You will be impressed by the orange day lily which has produced two heads this year, opening its flowers with their cheek-like orange petals one day at a time. My book on plant breeding describes the day lily as the most speedy and spectacular creation of plant breeders. Apart from its flowers, it is worth having for the brave show it puts up in March, its pale green shoots like lilies in the half dead border.

I have to thank Hilda, my stepmother, for introducing me to day lilies. I know she's no relation of yours, Daisy, but it's my belief that adopted relatives are as important as blood ones, and as my second mother and the only grandmother your father knew she played an important part in our lives.

A spinster when she married T at the age of sixty – they had been engaged in their youth – she had no brothers and sisters and virtually no cousins but coped admirably with the large and articulate family she married into. When Alex was only four and I had to go into hospital for a minor operation she and T took care of him.

It was a terrible Sunday when we heard that she had died suddenly while away. I was so distraught when I loaded the car to go over to my father's that I put in the dog food and forgot the dog. Your father, aged thirteen, came home very subdued in his best school uniform to attend the Quaker memorial meeting and the family lunch which followed. Your great grandfather, who had not expected to outlive her, was never the same again.

Sometimes I feel I was born under a Quaker star because in Hilda's life, as in my mother and father's, Quaker relief work was important. She spent years abroad in Greece and the Lebanon where her parents ran farm schools and traces of her sojourns linger in this house in the beautiful Greek embroideries I use as bedroom runners and the shepherd's dinner pail as I call it, a silver and copper container with a marigold etched into the lid.

Hilda's mother I never met but I feel I knew her. In her youth in Birmingham in the art nouveau period she carved the oak chest with the lion arms which is now your father's and which I hope will be part of your childhood as it was his. She carved on it the date of her marriage in 1900 and the two sets of initials. She must have hoped she was founding a dynasty and I like to think of you and your father as part of it.

This morning we could make pastry, using the rolling pin and board which resembles the little set I used to have as a child. So

41

much did it influence me that when I set up home in my twenties I found that I had chosen from all others the scaled up version of my childhood set.

There's plenty of jam for jam tarts so we might use up the gooseberry which will soon be superseded. I haven't any exciting tart cutters but I saw a fascinating set on an antique stall the other day. They ranged from about four inches in diameter to the size of my thumbnail and were enclosed in their own strong round tin. I was looking for a wedding present and nearly bought them as equipment for the pioneering days of marriage but perhaps these days such a gift would be misconstrued.

Another time, when you've mastered jam tarts, I'll introduce you to Ruth's Yorkshire mint pasties which contain the essence of summer just as spicy mince pies contain the essence of winter. Mint is abundant now; there can't be too much for the filling of Ruth's pasties, composed of chopped mint, brown sugar and butter. They are so good that after I tasted them I could never go past the mint bed without recalling them.

You can help me dig up the first new potatoes, not the ones specially planted at Easter but the volunteers which have come up in the wrong places. Some are no bigger than marbles, but that doesn't matter as I don't scrape them but just scrub them and eat them in their dressing gowns, as the French say. If there are only a few, I put them in a casserole with the first peas and beans and tiny carrots and call it an oven garden.

At home, when we had any delicacy for the first time, whether it was asparagus or strawberries or new potatoes, we used to wish. I think it was a vestige of an old Jewish custom, making a prayer of thanks for the first of any crop.

We can wish, too, over the first strawberries which always taste better for being picked by loving hands. Apart from getting entangled in the net, picking is a pleasure, exclaiming over the biggest or the most perfect. It's no modern pleasure either: in August 1837 the Ames family found in their garden near Norwich a fruit which, measured with string, was seven inches round, as Mrs Mary Ames related in a letter to her daughter Mary. 'When I see an account in the newspaper of any monster in either fruits or vegetables I shall not join the unbelievers as heretofore and cry out impossible.'

With new potatoes and strawberries we can celebrate our feast day this month, the feast of St Margaret of Antioch, patron saint of King's Lynn, observed on July 20th. I hope when you grow up, Daisy, you don't take against your name, as so many girls do. It is the name of pearls and flowers, of queens and saints, even if the life of St Margaret of Antioch is said by the author of my dictionary of saints to be a myth. Maybe, but just as Helen's beauty was enough to launch a thousand ships, so the legend of Margaret's virtue was enough to raise scores of medieval churches. It is almost impossible to take a drive in this part of the country without passing one dedicated to her.

In the American style you are Margaret the Fourth as you were named not just after me but after my mother and her namesake her Tante Grete who lived in Breslau, now returned to Poland. She died in her nineties in a concentration camp, having refused at my parents' behest to end her life as a refugee. She defied Hitler though by sending her silver and other valuables out of the country saying she would rather throw them in the River Oder than let the Nazis get them.

This afternoon if it clears up we might do some sewing, sitting in the basket chairs in the orchard near the cherry and near Kitty, Lottie and Patty in their ark. There is something very peaceful about hen noises – apart from their raucous cackling, when I always feel like fetching the oilcan. Did you know they purred? Well, something very like it. And watching them delicately stripping the grass heads of their seeds is also very soothing.

No doubt Pan will come and go as the mood takes him, lying near us when he feels like company and then retreating to the long grass when he gets too hot. Sometimes he arrives with a dusting of gold pollen over one ear.

There is a little pink thimble out of a cracker I have had in my workbox for years which might fit you. Try to acquire the habit of wearing a thimble while you are young. I never did and I regret it.

I wish I still had the strawberry pincushion made in China which fascinated your father as a child. It was very realistic, and had, linked to it by a green thread stem, a smaller strawberry stuffed with emery for cleaning needles and pins. I have never seen another.

I'll start you on a piece of plain sewing, an apron for you to wear on your visits here. I remember the one in green and white check I made at school at the age of eight. I loved sewing, despite the fact that I was left-handed, which made me the bane of teachers. I expect you'll be right-handed like your parents, and I shall be relieved. Even in these enlightened days, the left-handed are handicapped at every turn by the design of such things as telephones, kitchen knives and cheque books. When my mother was a child, her hand was tied behind her back to make her write with her right hand. She went on sewing with her left hand, but a prize she won for sewing was taken away when it was found it was done with her left hand.

I started to write an essay once about aprons which are becoming things of the past, though I still cling to them. Are they badges of honour or symbols of slavery? I listed all their uses: to protect the clothes, to wipe the hands on, for lifting hot pans, for carrying sticks or windfalls, to cry into, to throw over one's face (I've never seen this done except on stage), to take off on the arrival of a visitor to show that she is welcome, to provide pockets for women who are not allowed them in other garments. I found a new (old) use the other day when one of the hens got out and there was no stick to hand: I picked up the bottom of my apron and shook it at her.

There are a couple of sheets to sides to middle which will keep me busy as I do them by hand, preferring the leisure and quiet of pleasant surroundings to the busyness of a machine. I always remember the sisters in *Little Women* at their sewing, calling the seams after the continents and discussing them as they worked.

When we need to stretch our legs I'll show you the leaves of Mme Alfred where the leafcutter bees have been busy, cutting out neat circles to roll up for their nests. If you get bored, I might tell you the story of the tailor and his cloth, though I could never tell it as well as the Irish storyteller I heard on the radio. And for tea, surprise, surprise, there will be home made gooseberry tarts.

CHAPTER SIX

GRANDMOTHER'S FOOTSTEPS

August

The view from my window now shows unmistakable signs of autumn. The rowan berries are full orange and the birch leaves no longer have the green flush of summer but a dry yellowish tinge. Round the window, the flowers of Mme Alfred are outnumbered by the hoary seed-heads of the clematis. The robin sings its autumn ditty. The fairy apples are ripe and the squirrels are scrumping them. From my bed in the morning I can see them swing down on the end of a pliant branch of the sycamore right into the middle of the apple tree.

This month a succession of fine days have opened like morning glories and I am living on the shore of a lake, a lake which shimmers in the wind, is bluest in the midday sun and turns dull green at night. When the tractors came and harrowed the field across the lane, putting paid to the larks' nests and temporarily to their songs, I asked myself what crop I would most like to see growing there. The answer was flax, and my wish has been granted. It's just like living near water, the blue changes so often. First one patch came into flower, then the rest followed. The blue waxes and wanes during the day, reaching its deepest when the flowers are at their fullest. When the wind gets up there is yet another mood. Almost I can imagine I am back by my beloved river.

On this side of the lane there is a waxing and waning too. When I go into the kitchen to get my breakfast on a tray the chicory flowers are deep blue and bunched like little cornflowers. By the time I get up they are full wheels, bits of the sky cut out with pastry cutters. If it is hot, they are wilting and grey like me before midday. If it is cool, they flourish until late in the afternoon.

The chicory flowers play Box and Cox with the evening primroses which the French call beauties of the night. They spend their day in a state of dishevelment – their hair in curlers, so to speak. Then, in the evening, signs of new life appear. At sundown, the long buds which have split to show yellow reveal a petal and a stigma and then suddenly, while you are watching – if you haven't been distracted – flick open halfway towards their full beauty. It's the only time I know except in a slow motion film when you can see flowers move. But always it tends to be like a game of grandmother's footsteps: to happen when your attention is elsewhere.

The year after the Battle of Waterloo Keats was watching the same thing. In a poem written in the second half of 1816 he describes a clump of evening primroses:

> O'er which the mind may hover till it dozes;
> O'er which it might well take a pleasant sleep,
> But that 'tis ever startled by the leap
> Of buds into ripe flowers.

Perhaps one day you will spend the night here and watch the evening primroses open. The flower garden to the north-west of the house is at its best on a summer evening with the setting sun shining through the flowers. Afterwards, if it is a clear night we can take a rug on to the lawn at the back and lie down to view the sky salted with stars.

I grow tobacco flowers round the lawn, and if it is warm the humming bird hawk moths may well be hovering round them. And we may hear a rustling among the dead oak leaves rotting against the house and know that the hedgehog is on his rounds. I haven't seen him yet, but he has paid me a call. One night I left the front door wide open all night by mistake. I closed it in the morning and thought no more about it until, cleaning the lobby, I found the hedgehog's card, a dropping, beetle dry.

You can sleep in the little spare room which I furnished long before you were thought of. Sometimes I call it the blue room, after the blue and white Indian bedspread and the blue china handles on the cupboards. They are Mexican, with little birds on them, and made me look differently at sparrows ever after.

I hope you like the pictures. Over the bed is a black and white nativity scene in cut paper work sent from Vienna just after the War. It has the spiky look of much German folk art, the angels resembling pixies. Also over the bed is a primitive watercolour of yellow violas in a blue bowl, primitive because all the flowers are turned full face to the painter. I am particularly fond of another watercolour, a bird's nest with blue eggs in it near a bush of flowering gorse. It carries the regret though that someone long dead must have robbed a bird of its nest in order to paint the picture.

I bought it for five pounds at the first – and best – car boot sale I ever went to. It was at that car boot sale that I found a set of Victorian building bricks like the ones I played with as a child. Those have gone into Robert's branch of the family. I hope these will go down in ours. When I brought them home, your father was still a boy but I told him no, they were not for him; they were for my grandchildren.

But I am running on . . . When you arrive, Daisy, we'll have some lemonade, made from the old family recipe which I remember as a small child as one of the best things about a hot summer. My mother loved lemons and always had one in the house, a good rule for any housewife. She suffered during the War when they became unobtainable.

I've got lots of things to show you but the first must be the two tiny chicks which Lottie the broody hen has hatched. For days she growled at me when I checked on her in her coop in the mornings. Then, one day, as I turned to go, I heard her crooing, and not to me. I lifted her up very gently but I didn't see anything at first. I was expecting yellow chicks, not these dusty black ones, more like baby moorhens. At present they are identical; according to the books it will be six weeks before I can tell their sex.

I must show you the morning glory, flying its rare kites near the water butt, and the first flowers like quilled daisies on the *Rubus bellidiflorus.* Then there is the carnation bed. I love garden carnations with their masses of silvery buds and foliage, nothing like the pampered ballerinas at the florist's. When there has been a rain or heavy dew you realise why the red ones were christened sops-in-wine. This year there is a beautiful pale blush one which is my pride and joy.

In this garden I have had all the flowers I could wish for and I thank God for it. I need no flowers wilting at my funeral.

A few years ago I got so upset about the amount of heroin addiction – even afflicting the son of a friend – that I no longer wanted to grow opium poppies and rooted them all up. Now, after seeing the beauty of some scarlet ones in a friend's garden, their grey glaucous foliage reminiscent of wood carvings, I have relented. Plants can't help it if we misuse them, the addicted son is cured and I relish poppy seeds on the occasional challah.

I've cadged some seed of the scarlet poppy and also collected some of a fine maroon, almost black, which grows wild on a group of allotments. As both colours are there exclusively, they presumably breed true and it will be interesting to see what happens when I grow them side by side in the front garden. It is a problem worthy of Mendel.

Ever since I first heard the story of Gregor Mendel and his experiments in breeding peas I have been fascinated by it. It was one of the things which led me to specialise in science at school. It seemed marvellous that in such a simple way with little in the way of equipment, merely endless patience and time, the ability to select the right subjects for experiment and the intelligence to marshal the results, this Moravian monk should have been able to crack the problem which had been puzzling mankind since the beginning of the time – the way heredity operates.

What they didn't tell me at school was that Mendel was no ordinary monk and Brno no ordinary monastery. It was a hotbed of plant breeders and experimenters. His fellow monks included philosophers, mathematicians, mineralogists and botanists and there was already an experimental garden there. In fact, at one point the bishop threatened to abolish the monastery on the grounds that it was devoting too much effort to scientific activities at the expense of its spiritual life.

Mendel when he went as a monk to study at the University of Vienna took the widest possible range of subjects, among them mathematics, plant physiology and a special course in experimental physics. It proved the right preparation for his work which, exemplifying the saying that genius is an infinite capacity for taking pains, involved the growing of some 28,000 plants and the careful examination of 12,835. This peasant's son with a tendency to depression whose education was partly financed from a sister's dowry (he recompensed her by financial help to his nephews) is regarded as the founder of genetics.

His was no one track mind either. After being elected abbot in 1868 and becoming involved in politics he conducted no more experiments with peas but still found time to breed fruit trees and bees and develop an early interest in meteorology, making observations on such concerns of our time as the height of the water-table and the effect of towns on the ozone level.

Mendel must be turning in his grave at the way in which genetics is being misused now. One of the reasons why I have never regretted laying the foundations of a scientific education is that it gave me some idea of scientific method and dispelled the awe with which my generation has regarded scientists and which has been largely responsible for the misuse of their discoveries.

Science without conscience is but the ruin of the soul as Rabelais put it.

From Mendel we get the idea of dominant and recessive genes which throws light on human genealogy – how a trait can disappear for generations and then reappear when there are no more dominant genes to mask it. True genealogy would take you in 2, 4, 8, 16, 32, different directions, unless of course there is much intermarriage as with the Rothschilds or the Royal family. Only the Queen has a family history which goes back so extensively and even hers had dead ends where the genes of some unknown commoner joined those of royalty.

It is these dead ends, or wild cards, which are the most exciting. You have lots, so anything can turn up in your genes and those of your children. On my mother's side, for instance, we know next to nothing about my grandmother except her tragic fate. What we should have known about the Sackurs, my grandfather's family, disappeared in the holocaust. Only legends remain of

Aunt Grete, whose name you bear, of Aunt Paula, who was married to an impresario and rode a white horse in Unter den Linden, and an unknown Sackur who was assistant to a famous scientist (which one?) and bequeathed his abilities to four Cambridge graduates of my generation alone. Back in the mists of time, in the eighteenth century, a Simon Sackur was recorded at Kronstadt, the fort of St Petersburg.

My father's family is much better documented thanks to his interest and researches, and for that reason I find it less exciting, though I should like to know more about Aunt Eleanor whose self-portrait I possess. Your grandfather Steve's family, a band of Irish catholics who emigrated to New Jersey from the mining village of Bowhill in Fife, is a big unknown. Not all of them went on the second step of their emigration. I have just remembered your grandfather's story of how, the day they were due to set off, he ran away, not wanting to leave Scotland. A couple of older brothers who were remaining in Scotland were deputed to look after him when he turned up and send him on.

If his family came originally from County Mayo, as I am told most of that name do, it was probably as the result of the great potato famine, which makes two famines important in our family history. Your great grandmother was a McCluskey, a name connected with the Kings of Ireland, so they say. I know nothing about her except that her name was Janey, or Jeannie as they spell it in Scotland, and that she had eight sons and two daughters, the daughters called Margaret and Jane.

But that's only half your genealogy. There's all your mother's side. You'll have to ask her about that. It may prove more interesting than all of your father's put together.

We could have hard boiled eggs and new potatoes in cheese sauce for our lunch. I've never had a name for this dish: perhaps you can help me think of one. When you are old enough, I will teach you to make a cheese sauce. It is one of the foundations of cookery and I bless the friend who taught me the art and hence all the dishes based on it including soufflés.

I never make a cheese sauce without thinking of Pan as a kitten. He lived with your father but came to visit me sometimes and was the wickedest kitten I've ever known though I have wondered since whether, living in a squalid bachelor pad, he was just hungry. Once he sneaked into the fridge unnoticed. Luckily he had been there less than an hour when I needed something from it and got the shock of my life when he swung out on the milk bottle rack. He had eaten half a basin of dripping to counteract the cold, an example of the soundness of instinct.

One day after I had made a cheese sauce and before I got around to the washing up I found Pan had been trying to clear up for me. He had eaten a large part of the sauce left in the pan and also some of the birch whisk, apparently under the impression that it was the creature's bones. It took me years to find another birch whisk to replace it.

This afternoon if the weather's right we might go down the lane blackberrying. There are masses this year as the hedges have not been cut and the first are the best – later ones hide behind a barricade of thistles, nettles and spiders' webs. Like primrosing, blackberrying annihilates time. While I am blackberrying I am child and grandmother simultaneously, a span of sixty years.

If we have tea near the summerhouse we must listen for grasshoppers near the sprawling marguerites. I heard one last week for the first time in this garden. When I came, it was a desert of mown grass, no place for any grasshopper.

CHAPTER SEVEN

ON THE MOVE

September

The sun rises directly outside my bedroom window this month
and sparkles through the trees – all the more so if there is
a slight breeze. When the leaves are wet after a shower, the effect
is like Indian mirrorwork. On dull mornings, the hens perch
late and no longer nag me with their hungry croaking.

There is a harvest feeling in the air, the urge to reap and
conserve. Yesterday at the charity shop I found an old glass
water jug, slightly cracked about the handle, in which to make a
monochrome seed arrangement. I arrange nearly all flowers in
glass these days: I like the effect of innocent transparency and
the revealed line of the stalks.

Already some heads of golden rod are turning to plush and
the fennel is a study in tawny golds. The sweet rocket with its
long fine pods contrasts with the honesty with its spectacle-like
round ones. I wonder if it is the seed pods which gave rocket its
name? The clump under the old hawthorn shoots off in all
directions like an exploding rocket. A far cry from the mauve-
white scented flowers of still midsummer evenings which remind
me of ladies' smocks.

There are silvery lanterns on the shoo-fly plant *Nicandra
physaloides* which I nicknamed ghost flower until I knew its name.
It's still a bit early for the chinese lanterns and the delicate sprays
of montbretia fruits. I usually put them with one or two heads
of Gladwin iris and hoary clematis in a little black papier mâché

59

vase. When the climbing hydrangea is bigger it will yield heads of dried brown flowers which look exquisite with either the last roses or chrysanthemums. Another flower which dries itself is the *Euphorbia robbii.*

But today I'm going to use brass, not glass, for a live flower arrangement in the brass incense burner. I make a collection every year of all the daisy flowers available cut off short for a carpet-like effect. This year there are sweet scabious, chrysanthemums white and bronze, bachelors' buttons, tansy, feverfew, tiny erigeron and michaelmas daisies, the colours and sizes providing the variation and the shapes the continuity. I think of this arrangement as Scandinavian.

Our tour of the garden must start with the twin chicks which have been feathering so diversely that I am almost sure there is one of each sex. Black is becoming so much like her mother and aunts that I am thinking of calling her Etty after her aunt Hetty who died in the spring. Little Decker who is not growing so fast has silvery wings and no sign of a tail. Evidently cocks, like men, mature more slowly than their sisters.

Then I must show you the lemon peel clematis, flowering for the first time, and the grape hyacinth leaves, promising spring in autumn. You can check my count of the big clump of autumn crocuses. I make it twenty. A couple of years ago there were only ten.

The swifts and the sweet peas are gone. The elusive, evocative scent of sweet peas is for me the scent of summer and one sign of age is the reluctance with which I dig up the vines, wondering when if ever I shall sniff it again.

Since July the flowers have been a joy, picked nearly every day and dropped loosely into tumblers with a succession of different foils. Quaking grass, gardener's garters, false maidenhair, bachelors' buttons, bronze fennel leaves, honesty, late lavender flowers, cotton lavender, all these are good in their turn but by the end of the season stalks are getting so short that I like them best with their own leaves and tendrils which are then no sacrifice.

Inevitably, sweet peas remind me of my mother, whose flower they were. I am sorry you can never meet her, but in our family, with big gaps between the generations, we don't get to meet our great-grandparents.

Only one of her grandchildren took after her, and then the resemblance was startling, though Margot, like your father, was born after she died. Thanks to Margot, I now find it easier to imagine M as a North Country schoolgirl and student and as the idealist and suffragette who worked as a political organiser in London. She was a gifted public speaker. My father told me once that someone who knew her at this time said she could have been another Ellen Wilkinson, though you won't have heard of the small fiery redhead who made a name for herself in Parliament between the wars.

M's political career was doomed when she volunteered for Quaker relief work in the Russian famine and met briefly the Norwich journalist she was to marry four years later. Though a feminist, she did not believe as some do now that any paid job, however useless, is more important than caring for a small child. To adapt Omar Kayyam, I often wonder what's the job they do that's half as vital as the one they shun. Though she lived in the days of maids, and employed help in the house, that help gave her the time to be a magistrate and a member of the County education committee and to promote family planning in the days when it was in its infancy. She was appointed a magistrate when she was carrying me, so that I can say I sat on the Bench before I was born. All three courts she sat in successively were country ones in which there were many landed magistrates and she saw herself as the poacher's friend.

Before and during the war she worked for Jewish refugees, and for the Norfolk Rural Music School so that we were on the fringe of the musical life of Norwich. She played the piano herself, continuing to take lessons; many a Beethoven sonata or Chopin prelude recalls for me evenings when we were alone in the house, she at the piano and I in bed, already aware that such music would always carry for me such memories.

I don't know where she first encountered sweet peas but they ranked important in her life. She carried them when she was married quietly in the lunch hour on Midsummer Day 1926 and grew them with the help of the current part-time gardener in every garden I can remember. One year when she and my father went abroad in August I filled a copper preserving pan full of sweet peas to welcome them back.

The sweet peas were at their best when she died of cancer in August 1960. We stripped the plants for a great mound of them to go on her coffin, leaving the gardener to dig up the row while we were gone to the cremation. Also on the coffin was a little bunch of harebells, picked on Sheringham Common by three little granddaughters, a fitting tribute to someone who remained at heart a North Country girl.

For years, I couldn't bear to grow sweet peas, regarding them as M's flower and not mine, but then grief ripened and now I enjoy them with memories of her.

During your rest, Daisy, you may like to look at the postcards I have had this year from travelling friends and relatives. The stamps are not as diverse as one year when I had them from four continents but I think I have had more cards than ever before.

They have set me thinking about travel and about the mobility of those in the Western world, which is tacitly assumed to be such a good thing. I am not so sure. Konrad Lorenz wrote somewhere that in animals locomotion is the product of a bad environment. If this is so, then all the travelling so many people crave and talk about is comparable to the migration of lemmings or the agitation of disturbed ants.

Since I was brought by illness to a standstill I have discovered the joys of being stationary. You can't live on the horizon any more than you can live in the future: everyone must settle for the here and now, with just a few glimpses through the telescope or into the crystal ball to set things in perspective.

I am beginning to think that happiness is not expressed by simple plus and minus bookkeeping like Mr Micawber's, but is more like a fraction, the bottom figure representing our aspirations and concerns and the top figure what we do about them. In the happy person, top and bottom figures are the same, making it an integral whole. An imbalance – too much concern and too little action, or too much action and too little concern – accounts for many of the unhappy people in the world.

Wendell Berry, whom I have mentioned before, sees modern mobility as a war waged by industrialism on humanity. It not only makes us discontented at home and avid for package tours, it displaces us from our birthplaces so that children, even if they have both parents, are deprived of the support of grandparents and young people no longer live among those with whom they have grown up. They feel anonymous, able to do things they would be ashamed to do at home.

When I was a young working girl, living in a bed-sitting room, I read a book about China, *The House of Exile*, which made a great impression on me. Written by an American Quaker, the first half was an account of the years she spent between the wars in the depths of China as the adopted daughter of a traditional Chinese family, connected with hers by long trading ties. Her picture of the life of that extended family, bound closely by tradition and in rhythm with the seasons, affected me greatly. This was how human beings were meant to live, I felt.

Of course, all this was destroyed in China by the revolution and when I tried to introduce my friends to the beauties of *The House of Exile* only one saw in it what I did. Contentment, viewed from outside, is not often attractive. It can appear smug. Chinese women of well off families until this century had bound feet and their servants were equally bound. But, as I heard an Asian woman say on the radio the other day, Western women, while claiming to be free, do not recognise their own bondage to fashion, consumerism and competition between the sexes.

Perhaps, one day, when you grow up you will read a translation of the *Tao Teh Ching*, that poetic paving of the way of virtue, which contains this description of a Taoist utopia:

The country is small, but has few inhabitants, only tens and hundreds. Even though they have all the trappings of the age, they do not require them. The people venerate death, they are not driven to welcome it or to migrate to distant places to avoid famine and misery. Even though there are boats and carriages, they do not need to travel. Even though they have coats of mail and weapons, they do not fight. Savoury is their food, beautiful their clothing, simple their living and happy their customs. They may see in the distance neighbouring villages and even hear the cocks crowing and dogs barking, and yet these people attain great age and live until death in such contentment that they do not go to see others.

Meanwhile, as a non-traveller, I need to preserve my plums; the Victoria is groaning with them again this year. Perhaps you can help me. I gave some of the fruit last year to Thea and she gave me in return her mother-in-law's recipe for Victoria jam, which involves stoning and skinning the plums. It's a job that's much more pleasant for two than one, like most household tasks. We might do it outside if the wasps aren't troublesome. The sun has a kindness now it has at no other season. In winter it has pathos and in spring valour, in summer it can threaten but in autumn it is benign.

The plums have to be left overnight with half their weight of sugar so you won't be able to taste the jam today. Tomorrow, according to the recipe, I render them with the other half weight of sugar and the kernels of some of the cracked stones.

Very few of my recipes survive as given, and this is no exception. I was doubtful last year about the sweetness of Thea's recipe, so I made another batch as a control, leaving the skins on. One came out golden and the other red, and the plum-red as I called it was almost skinless, the skins having dissolved, and of a good sharp flavour. So plum-red is the preferred version from now on.

When we get tired of stoning plums we can go and watch the butterflies, now focused on the marjoram which has naturalised itself. I am trying to learn the names of the orange butterflies this year. Tortoiseshells, red admirals and commas are quite easy; the problems come with the gatekeepers, meadow browns, skippers, ringlets, walls and heaths. Here at the meeting point of heath and woods and farmland there are many possible sightings.

September's air is full of other transients: gnats and damsel flies, birch seeds and thistledown, pigeon feathers and dead leaves, the scent of bonfires and the sound of rooks. Not signs of restlessness, but illustrating Aristotle's dictum: 'All moving things proceed from rest and from necessity and moving things are all seeking rest.'

CHAPTER EIGHT

HOLD IT GOD!

October

There was a high wind in the night and this morning Pan was not content to lie on the bedspread but burrowed like a huge mole under the eiderdown. He has been spoilt since the day when, as a kitten, he dragged himself home after an absence with an injured leg and I let him lie on my bed because he looked like dying of pneumonia. Only a swing in one back leg remains of the injury, but I have never felt able to withdraw the bed concession.

Through the open window comes the sound of the trees. 'The trees sing for me, they are not hired,' as a Welsh poet wrote centuries ago. The sound of the wind in the trees was strange to me when I came to live here. Since I have had trees as neighbours I have begun to learn their different voices, which vary not only with the kind of tree and with the wind but with the time of year and with the rain which falls on them. In the spring, when there are no leaves on the deciduous trees, they have a thin light sound. In June comes the first full leaved sound for well over six months; after a heavy shower you can hear the leaves running like rivulets. Now, with the sap falling and the leaves drying out there are days when the trees roar like the sea and the earth feels like a ship sailing through the universe, all of us, people, animals, vegetation and micro-organisms very much in the same boat.

October blew in this year and I looked up the Beaufort Scale which I am trying to memorise. The branches of the trees were moving but not the trunks, and umbrellas would have been a liability – Force Six, a strong breeze. Later, the trunks of the trees began to move as well, turning it into Force Seven, a moderate gale.

Who was Beaufort? According to my biographical dictionary he was an Irishman, born in County Meath, the son of a clergyman. He joined the Navy in 1787 and was seriously wounded at Malaga in 1797. He spent years surveying the coast of Asia Minor and suppressing piracy there and ended up as hydrographer to the Navy. It was during his twenty six years in this post that he devised the Beaufort scale and became Sir Francis.

He must have known, if only slightly, one of my heroes, Robert Fitzroy, the inventor of the Fitzroy barometer and of storm warnings, the precursors of weather forecasting. Also a naval officer, Fitzroy surveyed the coasts of Patagonia and Tierra del Fuego and was the captain of the *Beagle* in which Charles Darwin made his momentous observations. My admiration for him stems largely from the fact that he achieved all this while subject to spells of depression. It got so bad on Darwin's *Beagle* voyage that he tried to stand down as captain and hand over the command but was persuaded to carry on. At the age of sixty he had an attack which culminated in his suicide.

Some October days have no trace of wind, but are so still that the trees look as if they were sculpted out of iron and bronze and brass. They are so perfect that you feel like saying, 'Hold it God.' That's not my idea but Ken Kesey's in his rambling novel about the lumbermen of Oregon but I have been reminded of it many times by the perfection of an autumn day. Such days make me ponder on the assertion in Dostoievsky's *The Idiot* that the world will be saved by beauty.

For most of my life I thought that ugliness, noise and anxiety were necessary evils. Now I am not so sure. Most ugliness, most noise, most anxiety are man's creation, products of his unnatural way of life, out of harmony with God's creation and intention. Beauty and tranquillity are our natural right, Daisy. Western man has got his values wrong.

In a book of interviews by young people with old people in the USA I noticed only one which showed awareness of beauty. It was with a man of the Amish, the sect which eschews cars and other labour saving devices in the belief that they do not make for the world God intended.

Likewise, the American Indians recognise beauty as the right response for the beauty of the world. Detailing the gifts of the gods, including 'beautiful skins and furs, corn of the rainbow colour and black clouds, mist, male rains', a Navajo song ends up: 'I am beautiful in gratitude.'

Last time I was ill and in great mental anguish, it was not my faith which enabled me to live another day. It was a poem by W. B. Yeats, the one about Lissadell. I found it in an anthology in the hospital library and copied it out and pinned it on my locker. The beauty of it acted as a salve on my sore mind. I think we need to recognise beauty as an aid to setting Western society back on the right track.

If ever I say anything like this to my friends they say, 'It's all right for you, living where you do. What about those who live in the inner cities, or in the third world?'

No-one should live in the conditions which prevail in the inner cities. They are a sin committed by us all. No-one should be homeless, underfed, or live in such a tumult of noise that immeasurable strain is imposed on them just in filtering it out of their nervous system. My prayers, my actions and my politics are directed to this end.

Dorothy Day, co-founder of the Catholic Worker Movement, said, 'God meant things to be easier,' and Peter Maurin, the other founder, looked forward to a world where it is easier to be good. They lived and worked in the inner city of New York and knew that much of the suffering there came from man's greed – the competition and exploitation which left poor people hungry and homeless. Even the overpopulation which is at the root of many problems could be attributed to greed – so-called 'recreational sex'. Primitive peoples who are intimately connected to the land manage things better.

Dorothy Day will never be an acknowledged saint because her life contained many of the things which the Church regards as unacceptable – abortion, attempted suicide, divorce and an illegitimate child. But she built on those foundations a life as holy as that of many of the saints. The Catholic Worker Movement, which has been called a lay order, has as its rule the seven corporal works of mercy and all the discouragement and exhaustion that they entail. 'Love in action is a harsh and dreadful thing,' Dorothy was fond of quoting, again from Dostoievsky.

Now living out of doors becomes limited to rare sessions in the summerhouse and living indoors a renewed pleasure, especially when there is a fire. If you came today you would see some changes. I have taken down the sea green linen curtains which act as sunblinds in the summer and put up the tawny velvet ones which in their progress from the house on the quay have faded to the colour of tarnished brass. I am in the process of changing cushion covers from the cool whites and greens suitable for hot weather to the reds and golds which winter demands.

I love the description in Mary O'Hara's *Flicka* books about the Wyoming ranch house being prepared for the bleak Western winter. The pre-war Wyoming of the books I found fascinating when I was young, along with the horses and people who enliven the landscape. I still read them sometimes for the wisdom they contain.

We should have to put on boots and raincoats for our inspection of the garden today, for even when it's not raining the grass and bushes are usually ready to wet you through this time of year. You can help me pick the last of the nasturtiums, threatened by frost any time now, and admire the two freshest flowers in the garden, the nerines and the physostegia, the latter playing host to the last bumble bees.

I marvel every year at the curled airy elegance of the nerines – how so much flower is packed into so small a bud. They put me in mind of snowflakes, soufflés and cellular blankets. But I expect you will know them well already. I like to put one head of nerines in a brandy glass with shoots of big variegated ivy. It looks like something which has come from an old walled garden.

The physostegia which I at first thought a little dull has grown on me, for what other flower looks so cheerful and unwindswept in an October border? It is like a friend one thought was rather unexciting but who proves in time of trouble to be the staunchest of them all.

The wind has threshed the honesty and the Chinese lanterns are almost ripe. You can help me tuck up the special plants against the frost, wrapping dead bracken round the verbena, the pineapple sage and the arum lily given to me by a friend just before she died. Thank goodness most of the tender things in this garden are getting hardened or killed off. If the first frost is late, as this year, summer and winter meet in posies, yellow and white jasmine, roses and chrysanthemums.

But you will want first to visit the twins. The pullet has developed fast and is now a smaller version of her aunts. The cockerel, after a dishevelled stunted adolescence is getting his act together and beginning to sprout some silvery tail feathers. He is becoming not the Golden Cockerel of Prokoviev's opera but a silver one.

One dark morning last week I was woken by a loud screech from the henhouse. When I heard a frantic flapping I thought the hens were fighting and one had fallen off the perch. Then I heard another screech and more flapping. After the third screech it dawned on me: Harold was making his first attempt to crow. There have been no more screeches on dark mornings but no doubt we have not heard the last of him.

We might go over to the playing field before lunch to see if we can find any mushrooms to fry with the bacon. The milkman was there the other day picking them into what looked like a hat. They grow in circles like fairy rings and though tiny are much more tasty than the ones you buy. That field is under surveillance all the year by the hawks hovering static on the wind's dynamic. On the grass, along with the mushrooms, are puffs of feathers where they have nailed their prey.

We might bring back, too, some larger feathers and leaves for making splatter pictures with a toothbrush and an old comb. It's over forty years since I last tried, but it will keep us busy for an afternoon.

The smell of fungi and wet autumn days takes me back to the slice of my life in the Lake District, evacuated at the beginning of the war. For my elders, it was the phoney war, the quiet before the storm and the time of the fall of France. For a child of nine who hitherto knew only city life, mitigated by a large garden, or the cosy pattern of a seaside town, the days in the lakes were an eyeopener. They were also to prove my quiet before the storm: my last months of freedom before being subjected to the enforced conformity of a girls' public school.

For the first time in my life I lived in an extended family – seven cousins, four parents and a nanny, the nanny belonging to the cousins. This was extended still further by visits from my mother's sister and her family, till then virtually unknown to us, living as they did in Newcastle. Education was at a PNEU school evacuated from Hull to a big house in Grasmere where I discovered the delights of working at my own pace, learning long stretches of 'The Ancient Mariner' and traditional ballads off by heart, copying great pictures and writing between lines in the old fashioned way. We were made both attentive and articulate by the system of having to summarise the contents of our lessons as 'reports' either verbal or in writing.

We ran free from the bane of organised sport on the edge of the ballad country. The fells were just through the back gate and many were the expeditions we made into the sodden woods, golden with larches, bringing back bits of vegetation to draw and examine under glasses, and toadstools to set on paper overnight with a hole for the stem so as to record the pattern of their gills.

I still remember the exhilaration of acquiring a new double lined writing book and the pleasure I took in neatness and the very writing materials. I remember little about the teachers because thanks to the system they did not interpose themselves between me and what I was learning.

At first we stayed in a large hotel which had been emptied by the war. The war filtered through only a little, in the adults' talk and in the paper planes made by the children. Our fathers returned south to their jobs or to war work and letters and stamps became suddenly important.

Everyone knitted, even Robert, though his scarf spent more time in the hands of sympathetic ladies than in his own. We made socks and pixie hoods and wore them. Brightly coloured felt was still available and we made needlecases and pincushions and gave them as Christmas presents. Making things was natural, social and born of necessity, not the compulsive solitary activity it so often is today.

Then our mothers went home to look after our fathers and the five youngest of us boarded at the school, with Nanny to help out as an extra matron. In the spring and summer holidays my mother took Judith and Robert and me to stay on farms. I spent my time in April unsuccessfully trying to see a lamb being born. Damp from the mother I often saw them but never actually arriving.

The summer holidays we spent on a couple of different farms. I think the one near Loweswater where we stayed in a little cottage with a garden full of phloxes and a nest of kittens, with spells on the moors picking bilberries or the chameleon cranberries, was the remotest place I had experienced up till then. Had I listened to the promptings of my heart I would have spent my life in such surroundings.

Life in Grasmere was the nearest I have come to living in a community and perhaps explains why I have had an unappeased hankering for community life ever since. With the Siege of Britain taking the place of the South Atlantic it was a little bit what life must have been on Tristan da Cunha in the old days – an almost enclosed system, even more enclosed in the snowy winters when we skated on the tarn and, when the deep snows froze, tobogganed down over the top of the shrubbery in which we had burrowed and hidden in the summer.

CHAPTER NINE

SPARE JOYS

November

It's so dark in the mornings now that I can watch the day break. Once when I drew back the curtain and opened the top window for Pan to leap in I surprised a fingernail moon with its accompanying star just above the treetops.

The moon hasn't had a chance most nights with the wind chasing clouds and leaves in multitudes. Each tree parts with its leaves differently. The mulberry, that wisest of trees, stripped long ago, well before the first frost. The cherry does it secretly, suddenly, sometimes in two or three nights. The big sycamore sends its leaves spinning down like those propeller toys that children like. The birches which dominate this garden part with their yellow leaves first singly, like tipsy butterflies, then in a golden blizzard drifting even through the windows. The ash still hangs on to most of its leaves. When they go, they fall piecemeal and lie white spined and shrivelled, littering the ground below like a charnel house.

Oak leaves must travel almost horizontally, so many pile up here after a gale, though the nearest tree is two doors away. Sometimes I slow the car for one as it sidles across the lane for all the world like a wakeful toad.

Yesterday when I went out early to feed the hens a strange sound from the sky made me look up. Waves of geese were flying over, their voices together sounding like the cry of the wilderness. The Chinese say that wild geese carry messages. But

I should have sent mine to you by the swallows which left long ago.

It's so much colder that if you came today our tour of the garden would have to be a brisk one. The chicks are nearly as big as their foster mother; at a distance I'm not sure which female is which, but Harold is unmistakable.

The Chinese lanterns brighten up the courtyard with their orange flames. The laurustinus is flowering well. Every year the flowers and buds remind me of chopped nuts. I must pick some for the little Regency plate jug which is so worn that the copper shows through the silver. I wish we could pick and sniff the brave flowers of the wintersweet but so far the two shrubs are shy of flowering. Not so the periwinkle which I call the starch periwinkle from the blue white colour of its flowers.

Chrysanthemums too this year are regrettably few so the main newcomer in November is the schizostylis, another of your South African flowers, whose shell pink spikes look improbably delicate for an English November. Mostly shell pink, that is. I thought they were all pink until two years ago when a beautiful red spike appeared. Not a bright and shiny red but the soft Turkey red which is my favourite red of all. Since then there has been no sign of it, and now I daren't give away or throw out any of the clumps until it reappears. At this rate the garden will soon be given over to them!

When I found that red spike I felt like Mrs Hegarty must have done when she first found the sport which bears her name. What an honour, Daisy, to give one's name to a flower. To be a grandmother and to give one's name to a flower – I can't think of many better forms of immortality. Now I've let out two of my wishes: I must hang on to the third, or it will never come true.

I have felt that leap of delight before when encountering a

new flower. Once, as a small child, I spotted an exotic spike in the cliff next to the promenade at Sheringham. I picked it as a small child will and took it home to be identified as a bee orchid – last remnant of an orchid meadow lost to the sea. Again, as a teenager, isolated in a village where we moved suddenly at the end of the war, I found the heavy dank clay there unfamiliar, almost hostile, even though it grew the finest tulips, pansies and roses I have ever known. In a part of the garden gone wild under army occupation I came upon some tiny cyclamen flowering. I did not know then of the existence of the species cyclamen and they seemed small miracles among the coarseness of that garden's growth.

When we come in, you can help me peel, and core the first damaged Bramleys to make an apple charlotte, one of my favourite puddings. I hope you like it too. There's soup for the first course so we need something substantial. And while we're waiting for it to bake we can clean the brass: the Persian table top, the lion's claw doorstop and the family candlesticks, so battered that I wondered if they had been used as missiles until I realised that something used night and morning six months of the year for a couple of hundred years and dropped occasionally was entitled to look a bit the worse for wear.

I like simple dishes like apple charlotte made from a very few ingredients. As the old saw says, necessity is the mother of invention. November is the month which brings us face to face with necessity – the need for light, the need for warmth, and the need for good food to keep out the cold. Most of the days are finger cold, as I once heard someone call it.

The Church sees November as a month devoted to death but I prefer to look at it as an exercise in relinquishment. There is something inspiring about the fall of the leaves. It's like watching a prize-fighter take off his outer clothes before entering the ring or, conversely, a welder take off his goggles and protective clothing after completing his task. It's as if the deciduous trees had heard Thoreau's call: 'simplify, simplify', and out of all their complexities of foliage were drawing the stark elegance of their wood.

For the tree, leaf fall is just a case of *reculer pour mieux sauter* but for us it sets an example of relinquishment. Most people in our culture have lives clogged up with superfluities: habits, activities, goods. Most of us are bound hand and foot, not physically but by our dreams, our prejudices, our fears. Our possessions too exert their own little tyranny of greed, anxiety and suspicion.

It was an important day for me, Daisy, when I realised that what you choose not to do is as important as what you do. A child wants to do everything: it is born to enlarge its horizons, but with increasing age the idea of abnegation should take hold. Artists know all about it – the space between the lines. Poets delight in it – the resonance of the unsaid. The Hasidic Jews have a proverb about it – he who adds, lessens – and the architect Mies van de Rohe put it succinctly: less is more.

When you have regained the power of choice from the pundits who shout 'more, more, more' then you can discover the joy of less. I don't claim to have done this voluntarily – illness took away much of my abundance. But when it was gone I discovered that less is often the key to delight, as in discarding things from a box so that the remainder can be set in order, or in inveigling people out of a crowded room so that the rest resolve into a related group.

So with taking things out of your mind – or rather stopping trying to pack so many in. Thomas Merton gives a clue to it when he says that if you have enough space in your life you begin to understand your own reactions and to be in command of them. We are surrounded by things invested with guilts, dislikes, desires, memories which we don't even recognise. Meister Eckhart said it even more concisely: 'God is not found in the soul by adding anything but by a process of subtraction.'

Of course, some people, the primitive, the happy, the young who have never been hard pressed, have never lost control of their reactions. I hope, Daisy, you will be one of them. And yet perhaps if you are you will never understand or relate to the rest of us.

What a long screed devoted to November spareness – and all evoked by apple charlotte!

But the spare life – what little I know of it – is anything but poor. It is a means of savouring the world as no rich or busy person can savour it.

When I was in my teens I found in the school library a collection of Mollie Hughes' recollections: *A London Child of the Seventies*, *A London Girl of the Eighties* and *A London Home in the Nineties*. I've got them here when you want to read them. They are all about spare living and the simple pleasures of life – an English non-fiction version of *Little Women*. Even today I often recall parts of them: how Mollie and a friend competed to see who could spend least on clothes in a year. And how her mother described mending as a work of redemption, which is how I've seen it ever since I read that.

I thought of Mollie as a contemporary of my mother, but now I realise she was contemporary with my grandmother; my mother was not born until 1895.

We shan't get any sewing done this afternoon because I'm expecting a visit from an old friend. I don't see Dermot very often these days but we've been partners in such various ventures as the conversion of an old chapel and the running of a junk shop. In fact, he is the best qualified among my friends for the role of Robinson Crusoe. He has turned his hand to so many things in the course of his life that he can usually be relied upon for practical advice and I pick his brains shamelessly.

When he comes, we must get him talking about his childhood, which is sure to interest you and says plenty about spareness – the involuntary kind. His father worked with *his* father in a Fife coal mine, but escaped a lifetime down the pit by joining the cavalry, which brought him south. His story reminds me of the old song 'I Know Where I'm Going' because Dermot's mother, a cosseted only child, defied her parents and left a comfortable home for the sake of this dashing soldier lad to share with him the privations and rewards of bringing up a large family.

> Feather beds are soft
> And painted rooms are bonny,
> But I would leave them all
> For my handsome, winsome Johnny.

Dermot and I grew up within streets of each other, but our childhoods were as different as if we had been on other planets. I wore liberty silk dresses for parties and apricot shantung (after Isadora Duncan) to dancing class while he as often as not roamed the streets barefoot. Once, when Guy Fawkes day came, he and two brothers drew lots to decide which of them should wear the one pair of shoes to the fireworks display on Mousehold. Dermot won, and trudged there in the shoes, two sizes too large. But he found the occasion lacking without his brothers, and went home to watch the rest from a window.

One of my childhood pleasures was to go with my brother to sail our model yachts on the pond in the park; Dermot swears that as a ragged boy he was chased away from that same pond by the park keeper.

As for food, Dermot remembers being taken somewhere every day by an older brother to get a glass of milk provided by the Guardians. 'My father had left the Army by this time. We had special biscuits too – biscuits which contained special food which we needed.' Despite this, he developed rickets and was in hospital for some time.

Meanwhile I was being supplied with rich Channel Island milk direct from the farm, supplemented by goats' milk during the war – goats' milk was unrationed. Biscuits – there aren't any biscuits now like pre-war biscuits – those oval sandwich ones with jam centres eaten with a cup of milk at teatime after the obligatory bread and butter. Glacé biscuits too with different pictures on them like snap cards. And those tiny dolls' biscuits which came in miniature cubic biscuit tins in our Christmas stockings. Somehow the dolls always seemed to have eaten them by breakfast time.

Dermot's main memories of biscuits after the nutritious ones are of buying a pennyworth of mixed broken biscuits from the International Stores not very far from his school. Mixed they certainly were, not only plain and sweet but cheese, but they tasted ambrosial to a hungry boy.

While I savoured my weekly two ounce sweet ration in the form of chocolate, he never saw his – the coupons were sold on the black market to provide necessities for the growing family.

Not all his memories are of hardship though. I may have been staying in a hotel on the Isle of Arran when the war broke out, but he was camping with his friends down by the river in a tent made of hessian sugar sacks. 'My friend's father was a despatch rider and he was called away immediately and they thought something was going to happen like an air raid so they fetched us home.' Far from being fetched home from Scotland, I was taken to the Lake District and did not see my home again for well over a year.

Even our memories of religion are different: occasionally I was taken to the Quaker Meeting House in Goat Lane, the place of which Elizabeth Gurney wrote in her diary, 'Goats was dis.' I remember it as a huge building sparsely populated by elderly people. There were only one or two other families with children and we went too seldom to make contact with them.

Dermot still recalls the beauty of St John's, now the Roman Catholic cathedral: masses with six altar boys and a choir of forty drawn from the two neighbouring schools. 'When they were all dressed in white there was a freshness of smell, not of Daz Biological, but of Sunlight soap and sheer cleanliness.'

One of eight children and father of seven, he could tell you plenty about life in large families. He never fails to emphasise the diversity of people. 'We are all different,' he says. 'You don't treat one child the same as you do another. What is a bad punishment for one child is hardly noticed by another.' Or, as a convict in a Russian book I have been reading put it: 'There is only one copy of each of us.' Shades of inner nature!

If he's not in a hurry to get back perhaps he will stay and join us for a bonfire. I've been saving the prickly sticks and dilapidated cardboard boxes for months. For me a November bonfire is a thanksgiving, not a Guy Fawkes celebration. The idea of celebrating the death by fire of any living thing is horrifying. So we must make sure the hedgehog hasn't chosen the bonfire heap to hole up in. He's not likely to, as there are much better places in this garden. And when it is well alight and the rubbish is nearly burnt up we shall feel that contentment which a controlled fire unaccountably brings to human beings who have made it one of the family.

CHAPTER TEN

OAK VASSALS

December

Only the klaxon of an occasional pheasant sets off the silence of the mornings now. On wet days Pan arrives with his coat cypress-scented, having evidently been sheltering under a neighbour's hedge.

It's strange to think of you in South Africa looking forward to midsummer while here we are approaching the shortest day – though to my mind that isn't really midwinter. The Russians, who should know, reckon winter starts on December 1st which would put midwinter in the middle of January. St Hilary's Day, January 14th, is by tradition the coldest of the year.

There's no doubt it's winter here. I keep the fire in on the coldest nights and one day last week, when the wind blew steadily from the east, extracting every last bit of warmth from everything in its path, I moved the hens into their winter quarters. They have left their draughty ark in the orchard for an old fuel bunker built of bricks and slabs and sheltered from the north and east. I call it their winter palace. Their living run is roofed with old double glazing panels so that they can bask and dust bath in any sun there is. When they were transferred it was the first time Harold the cockerel had encountered glass and he promptly tried to fly through it.

Except when the sun shines the garden looks a bit dreary. It lacks the sizeable evergreens and the russet of bracken and dried leaves which are the glory of the countryside this time of year.

The front garden though, with its lorgnettes of honesty and dogwood stems both scarlet and yellow, can still be magical when the sun shines low across it or frost transforms it into a crystal garden, Even on a dull day it can come to life when the birds arrive: flocks of chaffinches or long-tailed tits which sit in the old hawthorn and swoop down to avail themselves of the seedheads. Once greenfinches came to eat the catmint seeds and I hope goldfinches will one day find the teasels.

A cry as harsh as that of the cock pheasant belongs to the jays which, though rose and beige when at rest, fly in a magpie flurry of black and white. They are the enemies of small birds, but I feel more kindly towards them since I learned that they are forester birds. It is they who stash away acorns in the ground to such an extent that this garden is fast becoming a nursery of young oaks. I find it almost impossible to root them up: there are worse things I could leave behind me than an oak wood.

According to a cutting I have jays carry the acorns eight or nine at a time, all but the last having been swallowed. Between now and the spring they rely largely on acorns for food, and even though some get left, as the garden testifies, they have prodigious memories for where they have stored them. In Sweden one was seen to locate an acorn buried three months before and lying under a foot of snow. They would be world champions at pelmanism (I was pretty good at it myself in my youth).

Jays seem the most independent of birds but their need for acorns makes them yet another vassal of the mighty oak. The oak is itself dependent on them for its propagation, though there is another factor. Naturalists have connected the failure of oak forests to regenerate in France with the extinction of the wild boar. There's no such problem in this garden, where I play the part of the wild boar in kitchen garden and flower borders.

Our walk round the garden today would be another brisk one. There are hardly any flowers except the stars of winter jasmine, the chubby buds of the Christmas roses, the green icicles of the *Garrya elliptica* and the yellow sunburst of the mahonia. Still no flowers on the chimonanthus which should scent December. It is said to take seven years to flower but I hoped it would be kinder.

There's one surprise to show you – little seedlings of the magenta cyclamen coum which I shall need your fingers to sort out for me. I need your sharp eyes too to spot the bird sown hollies, many of which need transferring from unsuitable places.

The holly is my favourite evergreen tree as ash is my favourite deciduous one but some people seem bent on destroying it. That's why I plant it everywhere I go. I love all the English evergreens but most of all I love holly and ivy. I think in another incarnation I must have been a holly blue butterfly which in alternate generations lays its eggs on each, so that the caterpillar which hatches on ivy metamorphosises to lay its eggs on holly and vice versa. I thought I saw a holly blue in the garden last summer but have seen no sign of caterpillars.

Like holly, ivy is host to much wildlife. It flowers late providing nectar for bees and other insects and the berries ripen late in winter to the salvation of many birds. If allowed to grow thick, it also shelters them, like holly, and, like box, it houses the snails which nourish thrushes.

I must show you the ivy walk I'm planting. It might look to the uninitiated like a lean-to with corrugated asbestos roof and rustic supports once used as a cycle shed but I envisage it when the ivy has covered it as a cloister leading to a glade of evergreens.

The ivy walk was inspired by a delightful biography of Charles Waterton, a Victorian eccentric and conservationist. He spent much of his youth travelling in the rain forests of South America whence he brought back a half Indian wife. A devout Catholic, he went to Italy to see the Pope and came back impressed by the Cascini Gardens in Florence which, as well as containing people and traffic, sheltered a host of wild birds thanks to its luxurious quantities of ivy.

'I have profited by what I saw in Tuscany,' he wrote, 'for, on my return to my native place I began the cultivation of ivy with an unsparing hand.'

Waterton's home, when he wasn't living in the wilds of South America, was Walton Hall in Yorkshire, where the countryside was giving way to industry of the worst kind. He had a long legal battle about pollution with a neighbouring soap manufacturer which he finally won. He built a high wall round his own territory within which he made a sanctuary for wildlife, a little paradise, with a tower for martins, lakes for wildfowl and a heronry.

His management of the park was governed by his urge to shelter wild life, to make it into a kind of temperate jungle, resembling in its natural teeming balance the rain forests in which he had spent his youth. He shared my passion for hollies because they formed an 'unpenetrable retreat' throughout the year.

He was a host to wildlife. He didn't keep it, he invited it and enjoyed its freedom with it. Hedgehogs were imported, brought to him by the locals, whom he paid. Foxes were deported and the only creatures which did not appreciate his ark were the hares which, encountering barriers on all sides to their roaming, were found dead near the walls.

Unfortunately, his fellow Yorkshire landowners were not so enlightened. So-called sportsmen shot the herons and other birds as soon as they left the sanctuary and the saddest part of the whole book is the account of what happened to the park when he was no longer there to defend it.

By working on his two South American aunts, to whom the Hall had been left in trust for Waterton's grandson, his profligate son Edmund, a collector of papal decorations, objets d'art and early editions of Thomas à Kempis, gained possession of it, renaming it Walton Castle. The bailiffs were constantly in and out. To raise money he sold the woods to timber merchants, arranged shooting parties and sold off land as building plots. He also prospected for coal there. When he became bankrupt and could no longer live in England, he sold his son's inheritance – to the son of the soap manufacturer with whom his father had had that long battle to preserve the place.

The last part of Charles Waterton's life was not all sad though. It supports my contention, Daisy, that not all the best relationships are blood ones. Hardly had he written a despairing letter to Edmund about his double dealing over his marriage settlement than, as if in answer to prayer, an unknown sixteen year old apprentice turned up one morning. He had come on foot from Manchester where he worked in a cotton factory to see Waterton's natural history museum which had by then acquired some renown.

The owner was nowhere to be seen but the lad, Norman Moore, was admitted to the museum and before he left the butler brought him a tray of food. As he walked out through the park he met Waterton. They hit it off so well that he returned to visit the old man again and again.

He needed a father as much as Waterton needed a son: his parents had been estranged since his birth and he had never once met his father, an Irish barrister. He had been attending evening classes at a working man's natural history society and he and Waterton got on like a house on fire. He stayed there on many occasions and with Waterton got wet and muddy working in the park and investigating the wildlife it supported. He kept a journal of the days he spent there which gives the closest picture that exists of Waterton's life at that time and he was with him when he died. It was he who, after Waterton's death, rescued many of his letters and who republished his essays and his autobiography with his own biographical notes.

Norman Moore subsequently became Sir Norman Moore and the President of the Royal College of Physicians. He attended Charles Darwin in his last illness. I wonder if he talked to Darwin, who was also greatly affected by a visit to South America in his youth, about Waterton and his advanced ideas?

After we've had lunch and our rests I thought we might strip the lavender heads which have been hanging in the shed ever since I harvested them on a hot day in July. If you feel like sewing we could make the florets into lavender bags: I've got just the material – a dress I made in my youth of finely striped pink and white cotton overpatterned with navy sprigs – an eighteenth century print if ever I saw one. We could even make lavender ladies out of clothes pegs, copying one I picked up at a jumble sale, but I think we'll stick to lavender bags.

The lavender bushes come from cuttings taken from my grandmother's bushes. I have been thinking a lot about my grandmother's house this month, for it is being sold and the contents dispersed after being the centre of my father's family for over eighty years. So much so that in our family the words Claremont Road stood for the family as Buckingham Palace does for the Queen.

It has taken me until now to admit that I found it a forbidding place. I dreaded the Boxing Day parties rife with uncles and aunts and cousins as I suspect my mother did. Her problem was not, like mine, timidity and hatred of noise but the fact that she came of a background totally different to the nonconformists and teachers from whom my father sprang.

We played charades and pass the parcel and spin the platter and an excruciating game called My Friend's Chair in which the children had to go one by one into the sitting room in which the adults were all ensconced, each patting an empty seat beside her and saying, 'This is my friend's chair.' The unhappy child had to choose a chair and sit down on it. If it was the right one she could remain; if not, she was told in no uncertain terms (by boos?) and exiled once more to the dining room while another candidate went through the same ordeal. I'm sure a psychologist would find in this little pattern of rejection and elimination enough to cause any number of neuroses.

It all came back to me when I got my share of the carve-up, the mahogany dining table at which I am typing this and the chairs on which I had so often awaited my turn at these games. I was not a party though to an earlier game which centred round the chairs: an older cousin remembers at Christmas the portly sons of the house squeezing through the spaces in their backs to see if they were still slim enough. No wonder the carvings are so damaged.

It shows these pillars of my childhood in a vastly different light. So with my grandmother, the only grandparent I knew, I find it difficult to believe that the shadowy little person with whom I used to play spillikins was once the musical girl who planned to read mathematics at university until she changed her mind and got married instead. It was her family that supplied the didactic streak: her mother and father each founded a school, his for boys, hers for girls. My grandfather's family was in trade, that Victorian fate worse than death. Some of the money gained from groceries, however, enabled my great grandfather to share in the founding of a liberal paper which has become the region's daily.

When we've finished the lavender bags and managed to get the smell off our pungent fingers and had our tea of toasted muffins – I can still get them occasionally – you can help me set out the family crib, which doesn't normally see the light until Christmas Eve.

Your father knows it well, for most of the figures were part of his childhood. The seven brightly coloured Danish figures which form its core were found, strangely enough, in two separate shops. While Alex was still a baby they were joined by Finn McCool, brought back from Dublin for him by a friend who had been doing research there. Disarmed of his shillelagh Finn became a third shepherd and is still awaiting his crook.

Next came the stable, a well made wooden box set on its side and littered with straw or hay. It has a history too. It was made by my builder uncle to hold wooden bricks for his sister's little Montessori school, held in an upstairs room at that same family house. Some of the present city fathers (and mothers) started their schooling there, taking their morning walk under the trees along Newmarket Road.

There was still no manger, but while Alex was still a baby I bought a little wooden donkey and cart from Austria and dismantled it. The cart, minus wheels and containing a sprig or two of rosemary, became the manger; the donkey leans over it and the wheels are natural enough things to find in a stable.

Other additions followed – a star of fine wire, trembling on its stem, a tiny angel and a lamb, pot lid from a sale at Alex's school. A dove, some sheep and a sedentary cow were made by us out of modelling clay. Then came a big find – the Wise Men's three camels and the camel driver with his donkey obviously brought back by visitors to the Middle East and languishing in a junk shop. They are a little small, but that is the effect of perspective – they are kept at a distance. Even this year there was an addition to the company – a wonderfully woven basketwork ram obviously brought along by the shepherds so that they could keep an eye on him.

I haven't mentioned the bells, two typical Indian ones of unknown provenance. These were as important as anything when Alex was small and full of the excitement of Christmas because every time he stopped to look at the crib he would pick up the bells and ring them joyously.

This year on Christmas Eve I plan to make for the crib ivy chains such as I saw on a church crib twenty years ago. The priest there was very old and I suspect had made them himself. They're harder to make than daisy chains because ivy stems are hard to split but the effect is worth it. Another argument for planting ivy wherever possible.

CHAPTER ELEVEN

PIECING THE PAST

There's nothing to be seen outside when I wake up these dark mornings but there's something to be heard. It's the voice of Harold the cockerel, who still doesn't look like an adult cock – he's only just growing his waterfall feathers – but is beginning to sound like one. To the best of my knowledge he has never heard the crow of a cock but he's getting very near it. At first he was very flat, and the notes dropped at the end. But now he begins to display that cheerful bravura which makes the trumpet my favourite instrument. (It apparently sent the child Mozart into convulsions.) No-one has yet complained.

One morning last week Pan arrived outside looking like a snowy log, as in the E.H. Shepherd drawing of Eeyore. It had snowed heavily for half an hour and he evidently hadn't bothered to take cover.

The first few days of my new year are stiff with resolutions and lying in bed after cockcrow is a good time to take stock of them. One friend I asked about hers said they were a waste of time. Another wrote that giving up smoking and being less censorious were two of hers this year.

Censoriousness was on my last year's list. It was not one of the successes, though I did discover a wonderful quotation from the Desert Fathers which I have sent her: 'Abbot John used to say: we have thrown down a light burden, which is the reprehending of our own selves, and we have chosen instead to bear a heavy burden by justifying ourselves and condemning others.'

A few years ago I decided to adopt the motto of the Royal Norfolks: 'What the Holy Boys start they finish,' and this was a roaring success. That year, muddles were set in order, problems resolved themselves, chains shook themselves out, all because in trying to finish what I had begun I became chary of undertaking new things. With more finishes than starts, life became infinitely more satisfying and I hope that by now that resolution has turned into a good habit.

Main resolution this year is about tidiness. It has taken me a lifetime to discover that while a sweet disorder in a lady's dress can be a delight to a lover, in a house it is very wearing. I was brought up by a mother who, I used to joke, thought that godliness is next to cleanliness. I have at last discovered that what is really next to cleanliness is tidiness, which makes it much easier to be clean.

I can't bear superficial tidiness, where all the muddle is swept into drawers and cupboards. I prefer deep tidiness, evidence of an orderly mind, and superficial untidiness, a sign of work in progress. But I am beginning to realise the cost of even superficial untidiness. It's like living with a nagging spouse. Everywhere you look there is something demanding to be done. Which brings in procrastination which needs a new year all of its own.

At first light today the trees appeared swathed in starched lace and the main signs of life were the enormous molehills where the moles had followed the worms deeper in search of warmth. I don't mind their subversive activities, regarding them as part of the earth's functioning, and marvel that the small dead creature Pan left once on the lawn had been capable of such feats of mining.

Instead of walking around the icy garden, I thought we might take a tour of the house. People make a great fuss about investigating parish registers but often a glance round their belongings would tell them a great deal more about family history. Let us see what we can find . . .

First, in the corner over the little gate legged table with its shoal of eucalyptus leaves in a brown jug, is the icon brought back from Russia by your great grandfather. He bought it in the famine when people were selling prized family possessions in order to buy food. I sometimes wonder about the morality of that, but my father was a very moral man and he bought it.

Then there is the old miner's lamp which is serving as a book-end in the little blue room. That was your great grandmother's wedding ring. She got married at the time of the 1926 strike when the miners were selling their outdated lamps to raise money for strike funds. She put that cause before a wedding ring.

All the children who come here are fascinated by the little brass scales. They were designed to weigh letters but by my mother's time they had become a plaything. She played shops using the samples her wool merchant father brought home from his office.

In the book room Great Aunt Eleanor gazes calmly out of her gilt frame. It wasn't until I was painting a self portrait myself that I realised hers was one: the angle at which she is sitting and the triangle made by an easel in the bottom left hand corner give the game away. She's many more greats than one aunt; I must ask Robert who keeps the Copeman family tree for her dates some time. With her tall black hat with the purple clematis on it she has a dashing revolutionary air and I wish I knew more about her. Some prudish Victorian has painted a rosebud to cover her decolletage but at least she has survived in the family so far.

In the orange room are pictures of King's Lynn, of the quay where I lived for a dozen years and where I intended to end my days, but for the arrival first of your grandfather and then of your father. I am wedded to that river, thanks to throwing a ring into it, Venetian fashion, and expect to rejoin it when I die.

On the windowsill in the passage are the ferns, including the devil's claw fern which fascinates your father. Its silver shoots clawing their way out of the pot look very much like Pan's paws. It's sad that the devil used to be seen in the shape of an animal when usually he much more resembles a human.

In the same pot I have put for safety the fossil I picked up from the gravel the other day. It seems to be a petrified snail, split along its length to show both shell and occupant. I've never found a fossil in the garden before, nor have I ever found a four leafed clover. Something to keep you busy when the warm weather comes.

It would be easy to make our tour without mentioning the Persian rugs, those gardens of the desert on which I was brought up, and to which my life is keyed. To those who grew up with them they are not objets d'art but necessary backgrounds and Alex shows signs of feeling this too. (RLS and his wife are said to have set up home among packing cases, having spent all their furnishing money on a Persian carpet.) Each has its history, and though I have bought some, others lead into branches of my past. The lovely one in my bedroom, in pinks and blues and fawns, came from Hilda, my stepmother, and I hope will be with me till I die. It is more part of my world than any picture.

My mother's favourite – typically – was a very large one, in pinks and greens and fawns, and had to be sold for lack of space. The one in the living room, in reds and blues and greens in a very distinct pattern, came back with my Auntie Vi after the war. It was quite new looking when I first remember it, but over forty five years has faded to match the rest. The other living room rug, a squarer one, was once in my father's book room. The centre is relatively unremarkable, but the outermost border, not much more than an inch wide, is exquisite in hearts and lozenges of pinks and blues.

Persian rugs must be anathema to those who demand perfection. They represent the opposite view, the Muslim one, which says that only Allah is perfect and eternal, that if a craftsman approaches perfection he should leave some flaw in his work to show it is not God's. I think it is in the nature of man's work to be flawed as it is in the nature of man himself: like a recurring decimal he can never reach the whole. Gregory of Nyssa said this better: '. . . the essence of perfection consists precisely in never becoming perfect but in always reaching forward to some higher perfection that lies beyond.' The Hebrew word for perfection also means compassion, which puts a different complexion on several bible passages.

When you know how Persian rugs were created – how the nomad craftsman had repeatedly to pack his loom to travel on – you do not wonder at their vagaries but only that they were created at all. As for their colours, a friend of mine has the most beautiful piece of weaving, a source of marvel that any craftsman could create such beauty. When we turned it over, the unfaded back was in the crude colours of the bazaar. Time was the craftsman which had faded it into beauty. Time is the best of all gardeners, both in the desert and in the watered lands.

There is stone soup for lunch, I made some yesterday. Named after the Russian fairy tale, it contains something of everything and is a good way of using up all the bits which accumulate. I recently made a breakthrough in soupmaking, when I realised that in my urge for quantity I was making soups too dilute. Since then they have been quite tasty.

While you're having your rest, you might like to play with the garden puzzle which Alex had when he was small and which fascinates me as much as any child with its transformation scene. Done, it's a snow scene, with a bare tree, a wintry greenhouse, robins and children with a snowman. Lift the six pieces by their little knobs and you see the same children in the garden in summer, the tree with leaves and fruit, and the parents working with spade and lawnmower.

I often think how dull it must be to live in a country where there is not this dichotomy between heat and cold, darkness and light.

During my rest I shall go on with my reading of St Francis de Sales whose feast day falls this month. The gentlest of saints, who renounced estate and title and refused an archbishopric, he is yet a doctor of the church and the patron saint of writers, though I did not know this when I adopted him as mine. Centuries before St Thérèse of Lisieux he was a proponent of the little way and of starting from where you are rather than where you would like to be. 'Why build castles in Spain when you have to live in France?' he used to say.

In his *Introduction to a Devout Life* and in his letters, he is particularly helpful to women, perhaps because he was surrounded by them, to the extent to which he was reproached by other churchmen. Even as a bishop, he was dedicated to poverty – a poor man to whom he gave his best outfit complained about its condition. He used lots of simple examples from natural history – some of them sadly outdated – and he shared my passion for proverbs. '*Rien de trop*' and '*Festina lente*' were two of his favourites.

I like the story about his last meeting with St Jane de Chantal, with whom he founded the order of the Visitation and who shared many of his ideas. She had many plans and problems to discuss with him and probably wondered how they would find time for them all. 'Her orderly mind was ready to avail itself of every second. St François was as instant as ever. When she would speak he asked her to listen. But not to him . . . to his footman Charles waiting outside and entertaining himself by whistling a casual tune. When St Jeanne would have interrupted he would beg a moment's more silence to appreciate the unselfconscious grace of the boy's ditty.'

'It was like a scene between a Zen master and his pupils,' wrote Gerald Heard, relating the story, 'the master listening to a bird and then telling the anxious class: "the sermon has been preached, did you not hear it?"'

After our rests, we'll get out the patchwork bags, their cotton contents evocative of summer. The quilt I'm making for you when you grow up is in hexagons, a flower garden pattern, but you, if you want to do some patchwork, had better start with squares. What about a quilt for your best doll? Once, when I was in hospital, I made a whole set of dolls' bedclothes to go in a doll's cot Robert was making for his elder daughter. She's just had her first baby; I wonder if she remembers those dolls' bedclothes?

My quilt is only at the patchmaking stage but it is an exercise in recollection, the cotton pieces recalling the days of my youth.

This top, with dark blue flowers on white, I wore when I was carrying your father; this elegant gold and white shirt dress I bought one afternoon when I was waiting to collect him, aged eight, from school. Unsuitable for a quilt, but still hoarded, this flower printed striped muslin in turquoises on white was my first dance dress. It still speaks to me of the pains of being eighteen. It must have influenced the purchase of this nightdress in striped turquoise voile which I took with me when I visited your grandfather in Penang and saw him for the last time.

This blue and white check was my favourite gingham, but the shape of the dress was never right for my youthful embonpoint. This blue green patterned with white like a mermaid's scales belonged beside the river. It carries the carefree reflections of happy days, I didn't realise how happy at the time. This little piece of azalea printed cotton reminds me of Toni to whom I gave the dress – this piece was just a shoulder knot I took off. It, too, takes me back to a light hearted time. Toni and I once met accidentally at Thorpe Station, Norwich, a terminus, when we were both waiting for the same last train. We sat on a seat and were so busy talking that the train came in and went out again without our noticing. We had to go as far as we could along the line and then hitch hike the rest. The last I heard of Toni she was in Cyprus with a soldier husband and two little boys. I hope she is happy now and a grandmother.

That dark blue green with the Scandinavian looking flower sprigs was another maternity dress. I liked it so much that I went on wearing it for years. There is a photo of me in it holding the hand of Alex, aged about three, wearing a dark blue shirt, pale green shorts and yellow shoes.

This shirt dress in almost the same dark blue green, but overlaid with woven black checks Victorian fashion, was my favourite dress of all time and one in which I made a conquest. He was an Austrian musician in Lynn for the festival. His declaration arrived out of the blue after he went back. I met him again when I visited Vienna, my favourite city, and attended a concert at which he was conducting. I bumped behind him – terrified – on his scooter over the old Viennese setts but we never did get to Grinzing. He asked me just before, à propos of nothing, if I was a Catholic. If I had been then, Daisy, you might not be there in South Africa but there might be several black-eyed grand-daughters making music in Vienna instead.

CHAPTER TWELVE

RIBBONS OF SONG

It's still dark in the morning when I wake up. Between Harold's fanfares I can hear a trickle of birdsong. I open the window quietly and two green pips and a prrp confront me. A piece of the darkness jumps in and becomes Pan.

Flowers are still scarce after such a cold December. Every day I count the aconites. There are ten so far. The snowdrops are more abundant. This is the first garden I have had where they not only thrive but increase.

Every day too I look for the glimpse of blue mauve which signals the first *Iris stylosa*. Someone said of the strawberry, 'Doubtless God could have made a better fruit but doubtless he never did.' I feel like this about *Iris stylosa* among the flowers. You can pick a green quill from among the sword like leaves, put it in a warm room and watch it unfurl into a flower.

Algerian irises are sudden flowers, not like Christmas roses and snowdrops which are a long time coming. Most of the irises are sudden and the poppies, and aconites and Star of Bethlehem. Most sudden of all are autumn crocuses.

The trickle of birdsong gets stronger as the morning goes on. I once saw an African painting of a band in which the music flowed from the musicians in the form of banners and streamers. Any picture I drew of the garden this month would have to contain ribbons and curlicues representing birdsong.

I wish I could identify half the singers. My father could have

113

taught me, had I been ready to learn, as he taught me the yellowhammer's refrain: 'A bit of bread and no cheese.' I know the thrush and blackbird and the dunnock, an undervalued singer. I heard the chiffchaff the other day – it must have been – and I know the tits which go tsi-tsi-tsi and see-saw-see-saw.

In an old book I found a whole song attributed to the thrush which brings back the spaciousness of pre-war afternoons:

> Get up, get up, get up,
> Run along, run along,
> Time for tea, time for tea
> Tea, tea, tea, tea,
> Don't be late, don't be late.

The thrush's song is getting rare these days, though I try to make my garden thrush friendly and a pair were foraging here the other day. A garden without thrushes is no garden – but then I say that about cats.

The woodpigeons' monotonous reiteration has any number of interpretations: there has been a whole newspaper correspondence about them. I will leave you to decide what they say.

This spring there is still no sign of a nest in the tit box outside the living room window. There hasn't been a nest in it the three years it has been there and I think this summer I shall move it. It has not gone unused though. When I opened it last summer I found layer upon layer of tiny droppings testifying to its use as a tits' night shelter. One autumn evening I opened it at twilight and shut it again hastily, for inside a tiny bird was cowering.

Lately I have been thinking a lot about shelter. To come from a house with a walled garden to one where the front garden has

not much between it and the North Pole, and feels that way in a
northerly wind, is to be brought up against the importance of
shelter. I've tried to provide it with a country bank and hedge
but to little effect so far. Many's the ailing plant I have moved
from front to back garden to see it flourish in the absence of
cold winds.

The summerhouse, too, demonstrates the value of shelter.
Swivelled in winter to face south east and south west it catches
all available sun and is as warm as an oven on sunny days, even
when there has been frost. I have had tea in it twice already this
year.

Tea in the summerhouse, that epitome of easy living, while
others live and die on the streets. Shelter is as necessary as food
and drink, and I am sure that many of the inhabitants of
cardboard cities would not be there but for the lack of such
succour when they were most in need.

I see love as a microclimate, to use the environmentalists'
jargon, protecting and fostering as walls and hedges do in a
garden. 'It is in the shelter of each other that the people live,'
runs an Irish proverb. It is in watching the plants in my garden
that I have come to understand it.

If you came today we should go first to the henhouse to see if
Etty has laid another of her tiny eggs. She started last week and
has been shaming the older hens by laying almost every day. It
seems incredible for her to be producing eggs when, like Harold,
she herself was an egg only six months ago, brought home in
an egg box. The chore of gathering eggs has never palled on
me and I often wonder which was shaped for which, the hand
for the egg or the egg for the hand.

Then we can have an aconite count and a snowdrop count
and perhaps pick a few of the snowdrops and arrange them

with some of the flowering heaths in one of the little liqueur glasses my parents brought home from Germany before the war. The magenta cyclamen are ready to pick too if I could find a container small enough for them. A thimble would be about right.

The bread is running out, so you can help me make some more. I've got some yeast, and there's a warm fire to raise it by. I wonder what you'll make of kneading it: it always feels alive to me, the next thing to living flesh and a reminder of the place whence we drew our first nourishment. I know Pan feels it is alive, because I left him once by the fire with a bowl of dough working on the hearth. When I came back the dough had erupted over the rim of the bowl and Pan was nowhere to be seen – he had taken refuge under the stool where he goes when he is frightened. I have had the same sensation watching a molehill in the making.

You'll enjoy greasing and flouring the tins, and cutting up the dough to make rolls. I have two little tins which make perfect miniature loaves, just like I used to have when I was a child. Thursday was baking day, and I looked forward when I came back from school to finding a newly baked miniature loaf waiting for me. I hadn't found the tins when Alex was small, so he didn't have the pleasure of cutting and buttering his own slices.

You can scrape the bits of dough left on the bowl too and bake them in a patty pan as a special loaf for the hens.

I hope the bread will turn out nice and light and not, as my friend Ruth puts it, 'heavy enough to make a duck sink'. She makes marvellous bread herself and has done for half a lifetime.

We might go round and visit her this afternoon. It's too cold to garden, but well wrapped up we could take a walk round the candlestick, as they say in Norfolk, and pick up kindling for Ruth on the way back. There's never any shortage of sticks: I seem to be the only person who gathers them.

If you lag on the way back, I'll tell you about your compatriot Eugène Marais and his discoveries with ants – what a difference it makes to them whether they are on their outward or homeward journeys. When they are on their way home they can carry much bigger loads and cross much greater distances. I suspect humans are the same.

Ruth doesn't live quite next door, but she is the ideal neighbour, wise and caring and generous. She made the headlines a couple of years ago when at the age of seventy five she went to camp in the middle of the desert in protest against the Gulf War. I took her into town to catch the London bus early one dark winter morning and wondered if I would ever see that dauntless little figure again. Her knapsack was nearly as big as she was and she could hardly lift it. (This problem was solved when it was stolen almost within minutes of her arrival in the Middle East.)

I was reminded of Vanzetti's statement that we have war because we are not heroic enough for a life without it.

You'll find her very interesting to talk to. She's had a varied life, surmounting failure in the eleven plus to become a teacher, and finally head of a village school in the Yorkshire Dales. She could tell you many a tale about her children there.

She is a Quaker, and an untiring campaigner for the underdog, particularly political prisoners. Her opposition to war hasn't wavered since the day her father lost his job in a Birmingham factory because he refused to change over to making armaments. If only there were more like him.

Twice widowed, but with no family of her own, Ruth has adopted the world as her grandchild and responds to every appeal with immediate generosity. Who else could you find simultaneously corresponding with a man on death row in Alabama and a balalaika teacher in Russia, visiting a man crippled with multiple sclerosis, feeding the birds and boycotting banks and multinationals who do not share her high moral standards?

Occasionally her trusting nature, which is the despair of some of her friends, is abused, as when she let a tramp occupy her caravan. But she does not let it sour her. 'I'd rather be taken in sometimes than refuse help to someone who needs it,' she says.

If Quakers had saints, Ruth should have as her patron the New Jersey Quaker John Woolman, whose peace testimony took him on visits to the American Indians in the backwoods at the time when they were involved with both sides in the war between the English and the French. His testimony against slavery sent him travelling in the Southern colonies among slave owners and slave traders. It was his refusal to live on the produce of slaves which led to his wearing undyed clothing, by which he became singled out. He even refused the hospitality offered by Quaker slave owners and insisted on paying for it, a gesture painful to both sides.

John Woolman set sail for England on his last mission in 1772 without waiting for the birth of his first grandchild, to his only daughter who had married his orchard assistant. Even during his voyage he found more cause for concern. Insisting on travelling steerage, he was later to expose in an essay the appalling living conditions of ships' crews, conveniently ignored by other travellers. The treatment of the post boys and the horses on the English stage coaches had already determined him not to travel by them or to have any mail sent by them and he made his English journey from London to Kendal and back again to York on foot, enabling him to learn much about the conditions of the English poor at the time of the enclosures.

Ten years before he had written in *A Plea for the Poor* (not published until thirty years later) words which despite their awkward phrasing accost us across two centuries:

To see our fellow creatures under difficulties to which we are in no degree accessory tends to awaken tenderness in the minds of all reasonable people, but if we consider the condition of those who are depressed in answering our demand, who labour out of our sight and are often toiling for us while we pass our time in fullness; if we consider that much less than we demand would supply us in all things needful, what heart will not relent or what reasonable man can refrain from mitigating that grief which he himself is the cause of when he may do it without inconvenience?

He died at York of smallpox, nursed devotedly by his last hostess, Esther Tuke, and her step-daughter Sarah. Samuel Taylor Coleridge, who read much about the Americas with the idea of going out there to found a community, wrote of him in 1797: 'I should almost despair of that man who could peruse the life of John Woolman without an amelioration of heart.'

My life would certainly have been different if I had not read a biography of Woolman at the age of sixteen. I hope one day you too, Daisy, will appreciate it.

CHAPTER THIRTEEN

YELLOW RIVER

March

The sun again rises opposite my bedroom window this month and on fine days a lemonade sunrise glows through the leafless trees and silhouettes the firs which in summer are hidden behind them. On days when there is a little wind they sway like metronomes and the bare branches of the other trees take on a writhing distraught air as they wait for the softening green drops of April and the green floods of May.

The rowan buds are the first to break. One day this week, the twigs were endless. The next, each ended in a discernible white dot. Now these buds are unfolding, complex and furry like the sticky buds of horse chestnuts. Below the window, Mme Alfred is sprouting generously and big shoots have appeared on the *Clematis macropetalla*.

The weather changes so rapidly that if it were sunny when you came this morning I think we might abandon the house jobs and take to the garden. As I always say about the washing up, the housework won't run away. The warmth of the convalescent sun brings out the new scents of the earth and it is even possible for the first time in the year to take off one's coat while working in a sheltered place. Pan is already enjoying his first dustbaths.

You might like to help me sow some seeds. There are masses waiting to be sown. I am always afraid that one year I might forget something important and have to go a whole year without one of the garden's vital components.

The broad beans and the sweet peas are already in, and the tiny tobacco seeds are in a tray on a sunny windowsill. This year I am embarking on tree lupins and seakale. Tree lupins are one of my earliest memories – I used to play underneath them – but I only realised recently that their scent is not the peppery scent of Russell lupins but more like the haunting fragrance of a beanfield. Seakale is an unknown quantity. That's the lovely thing about gardening: there's always something new to try.

We mustn't forget the mignonette and the nasturtiums (though perhaps it's a little early for these) and the night scented stock. There are peas and kohlrabi waiting to go into the kitchen garden and salads if I can find room for them. The winter salads are still occupying the frame. But already the salad burnet and the sorrel are sprouting well and before we go in we can walk round the garden with the blue enamel saucepan and gather a salad wet with dew from them and the welsh onion tops and the land cress and lambs lettuce in the frame.

Before we go in, too, we must take the fir apple seed potatoes out of their winter nest in the apple store and put them to chit in seed trays in Pan's house, the little octagonal summerhouse which triples as hen food store and garden shed. It's late to put them out: I usually set potatoes on Good Friday, just as I usually plant bulbs for the house on All Saints Day for no better reason but that then I remember to plant them and know when I put them in.

While we are outside, too, you can help me find the first split daffodil buds which are another of the year's landmarks. I put the first daffodils almost up to their necks in a tumbler with a twist of big well patterned ivy leaves. Ever since I saw them arranged like this in an antique shop ivy has been my favourite foil for daffodils.

Soon the bulk of the daffodils in this garden will be flowering inside the front bank where I have mustered them in what I like to think of as a second yellow river. River seems the right collective noun for daffodils, as encampment fits foxgloves, tangle marguerites, gaggle nasturtiums and kremlin tulips.

Alas, there will be no kremlin of red tulips in the front garden in May as I had planned. For the second year running, my newly planted tulip bulbs have vanished and I think the culprits are the voles which live in the front bank. Pan stalks them for hours sometimes but they elude him. Next time I must see what dipping the bulbs in paraffin or covering them in soot will do.

The voles' relatives, the field mice, have been active too, invading the cupboard under the sink. Several times I have found a desperate mouse racing round and round in the pail where I collect material for the compost heap and have had to carry it outside and tip out the captive, first making sure that Pan wasn't watching, and admonishing it – in vain – not to return. They have even used the cupboard as a larder, leaving a pile of empty cherry stones like something out of Beatrix Potter.

With the salad for lunch we could have hardboiled eggs stuffed with grated cheese or marmite, whichever you prefer. The hens are laying well; last week they broke their all time record with twenty one eggs in seven days which isn't bad for four little bantams, three of them in their third season. There won't be so many again, as Patty has gone broody, another sign of spring.

This afternoon, whether it is fine or not, we shall have to chop the Seville oranges for marmalade. I got them out of the freezer last night and they can't wait. Thanks to the freezer, January's job has become a movable one. I usually save it for the cold light afternoons of March or April.

I've got two sharp knives – you can have the left-handed one if you need it. I hope you won't succumb to the prevalent distaste

125

for laborious jobs. Done in company, the separating out of pith and pips and the slicing of the softened peel can be an occasion for voyages of the imagination.

We could sing old songs, or our own. Alex and I used to enjoy improvising our own words to old tunes. I can remember our singing a dirge for our much loved Timmie cat calypso style when we had to go somewhere in the car the day she died. We could compose a Seville orange chopping song. Or we could tell stories of the lives of things. A famous Victorian writer related the adventures of a ten guinea watch, and a modern poet has followed the fortunes of a ten pence piece which attained glory by being used for the toss at Wembley. *Black Beauty* is this sort of book, but I wept so much at my first reading of it that I could never read it again.

Or we could relate incidents from our own lives. What would yours be, I wonder? I could tell you about the place of which daffodil time always reminds me: the garden of the house where I lived between the ages of six and fifteen. The daffodils which grew in the orchard there were old fashioned kinds, tall, graceful and delicate, which danced like Wordsworth's, nothing like the stiff overbright overlarge varieties of today. I spent hours among them, picking them, counting the different varieties and deadheading them.

The whole garden was a Victorian one, planted with forethought, imagination and generosity by a gardener who would never live to see it in its prime. That we enjoyed. It fulfilled Pope's specifications:

> Let not each beauty ev'ry where be spy'd,
> Where half the skill is decently to hide.
> He gains all points, who pleasingly confounds,
> Surprises, varies, and conceals the Bounds.

and it so shaped my idea of what a garden should be like that I see echoes of it in this much smaller garden today.

I would like to take you round that garden, for like all good gardens it was made to be walked round as well as to be sat in and played in and worked in.

It was totally enclosed, and the number of trees and hedges which bordered it would have horrified the labour grudging gardener of today as much as they delighted the children who used them as secret corridors along which they could slip unseen. Along the front, near the bus stop where the big double deckers called frequently, were red mays and a big pink chestnut tree which even I, a timid child, could climb a little way. Shrubberies, too, screened the lawn which doubled as a tennis court and gave a southern aspect to the house, built end on to the road.

Continuing along the gravel past the front door you passed a space where I suspect there was once a conservatory. Why else would there have been a small glass door – not a french window – at the end of the sitting room? You passed between two tall hedges into a sunny fruit garden where the bees guarded the strawberry and asparagus beds and a few overspill apple trees crowded the gooseberries between the box edgings. My mother's four herbaceous borders lined the path as it continued towards the orchard and her rosebed edged with Mrs Sinkins pinks and bedded with violas was discreetly concealed behind one of them. There is nothing uglier than a rosebed out of season.

Passing between two large laurustinus bushes you mounted slightly to the orchard. The incline was just enough to give us hours of fun when the snow froze, tobogganing down and seeing how far we could get the sledge to travel. The orchard itself, wonderful enough in daffodil and fruit blossom time, was a masterpiece when the fruit ripened. It had been planted with great thought, the varieties of the trees recorded on metal tags, and with careful harvesting and storage there was a winter's treasury of eating and cooking apples, pears and plums. In the far corner was the *pièce de résistance*, an apple house built of reed thatching, its reeds purloined occasionally by Robin Hood and his men for arrows. Wary of ladders, I was the one who usually sorted and laid out the fruit, and the smell of sweating apples still brings back memories. One Christmas during the war, when there was almost no imported fruit, my father gave each member of his depleted editorial staff a chip basket of Coxes and a jar of honey.

But we are only two thirds of the way round the garden, Turn right at the top of the orchard near a green summerhouse through another hedge partition and you come to a big poultry house and run and beyond it the compost enclosure. Used before the war as a playhouse – it was fine for Peter Pan and Wendy – the chicken house came into its own in wartime as the home of hard-laying white Leghorn cross Rhode Island Reds.

Turn right again and you are walking back towards the garage on one or other side of a productive vegetable garden. Linked to the house by a garden shed and a yard with fuel shed and clothes lines the garage had its own drive which was, of course, that essential for a Victorian house of any size, the tradesmen's entrance. It had white horse chestnuts and scots pines along its northern boundary, a couple of hydrangeas near the garage and our little gardens and a sandpit through which the alstroemerias insisted on growing.

It was an appropriate place for our family for my father came of a family of gardeners. His grandfather, Daniel, was painted by Munnings in his garden with his dog Trimmer. The seat on which he was sitting is still in the family. A rather tipsy Munnings arrived one day to look at the picture with an idea of including it in his autobiography but that is another story . . . Daniel's younger daughter, my great aunt Dora, had a little house in Sheringham with a tiny garden when I knew her, and some of my own plants, like the sweetbriar and the moss rose, are descended from hers.

It is in our Victorian garden that I like to remember T, whose birthday was March 21st, the first day of spring. It was there that he was in his prime, I think, tending bees and harvesting apples in the intermissions between editing a morning paper and firewatching when necessary. He had another flowering in a sheltered Sheringham garden after his second marriage but that was the Indian summer of an old man.

I don't think he would have minded my describing him as a Wellsian character when young, an earnest innocent fellow for whom an academic career was not financially possible. Instead he went to work on the local newspaper with which the family was connected, being quickly promoted to sub-editor. I cut my teeth on the stubs of the thick yellow subbing pencils which littered our nursery but I never saw a full length one.

Many of his stories about his youth were self deprecatory, like the one about how, as an army clerk near the front line in the first world war, he made himself an unofficial dugout under the office floor and got trapped in it when an officer arrived. Or how, when, a keen archaeologist, one of his best finds was spotted by his expert friend W.G. Clarke edging a garden path after T had rejected it.

He was an ardent sailor and naturalist and one of his tales related to the 1920s when he and some friends of his own age were spending a week sailing on the Broads. They were to be visited one day by some rather stuffy friends of their parents' generation, and duly moored near the station the night before. T and another were delegated to meet the train.

For some reason, incredibly for my father, they were a little late and saw the train chugging away from the station. When they got there there was no sign of their visitors and they returned cockahoop along the raised path and when they got within sight of the boat began to wave and dance, chanting, 'They haven't come, they haven't come.'

Suddenly they saw their dignified guests on a path at the lower level converging on the boat. The rest of the day was spent in the frosty shadow of that moment.

T's organising ability was in evidence all his life, whether as an army clerk helping to arrange the Red Baron's funeral, after the war starting an international pen friend organisation, editing first an evening then a morning paper or, in his retirement, reviving a local Adult School and encouraging the building of a Quaker Meeting House. He started to write his memoirs, but had left it too late. The essential record of his life is in his diaries, which he left to the Norfolk Archives, and in the Norwich files of the newspapers on which he worked.

Born in September and March, the two equinoctial months, my parents were as different as the two poles. My relationship with T was marred by the fact that I wanted to be like my mother. Instead, I inherited from him the traits which I would rather be without: hypersensitivity, apprehensiveness, pessimism and a capacity for love verging on the suicidal. Diluted enough in my descendants perhaps they will become assets and not the reproach to me that I unreasonably made them towards him.

CHAPTER FOURTEEN

SUNDIAL DOWRY

April

So you're coming home! Your father's phone call, like the one a year ago which launched these letters, has put a limit to them. When you fly into Heathrow and drive down to stay with me I must take leave of the Daisy I have been writing to, sometimes child, sometimes adult, and welcome Daisy the baby. I may not live to know you as a woman but I have talked to you as one in here.

Already the year begins to repeat itself. The japonicas are bursting their coral and jade bubbles just as they were when I lit the living room fire and the telephone rang. The fire is waiting to be lit again this Sunday morning. Pan is still curled up on my bed in the sun, legs and tail plaited.

Tomorrow, instead of going out to look for a teether for you, I shall hunt for a small chair. I know you're not ready to sit in it just yet, but in no time at all you'll be glad to have your own place in the room.

We must remember when you are a bit bigger to get a photograph of you standing beside the sundial in the front garden. I have one of myself with it taken nearly sixty years ago, and one of your father when he was not much taller than the pillar.

I shan't show your father these letters, conceived over the washing up, scribbled on the backs of envelopes and stowed in my apron pocket. He would find them a bit bland, to use the

133

fashionable word. Like the sundial, they count only the sunny hours. But I see what I have written less as a sundial's momentary record than as a legacy – a dowry – for you and you do not bestow unpleasant things on those you love.

I wish I could endow you with patience, Daisy, but I am afraid only life can teach you that. Only time can teach you the importance of timing. Life for the young is three dimensional – to impatient youth anything that isn't happening now is never going to happen – and only time can teach you to see life in four dimensions.

The old are notorious for their opposition to many trends. But it is only they who have the span of life to see those trends in perspective. It is the difference between a barograph and a barometer. I have used a barometer most of my adult life, but my father had a barograph and one of the first things I used to do when I went to visit him was to go and look at it. Its graph put the reading on my barometer into the context of time and gave much more indication of what the weather was doing. The old, like the barograph, can put events in context. They know something about trends and patterns, that things have not always been thus and will not be, that seemingly impossible ideals can be realised, and seemingly impregnable institutions can come to grief.

How little when I was young did I understand the importance of timing, repeatedly trying to solve problems in three dimensions which could only be solved in four. So often I did the wrong thing because I lacked the patience to wait for the right opportunity. How can we possibly recognise the right summer dress, the right work, even the right man, if it or he has not yet put in an appearance? When this time comes, if we are reasonably decisive, we shall have very little doubt about it.

The garden, that metaphor for life and religion, exemplifies this repeatedly. I search and search for the right place for a new shrub – there isn't one. A year or two later, something has died or been moved, even a new wall has been built, and there is the right place after all.

Making a person is very like making a garden. At first the possibilities seem endless. One is not aware of any limitations of soil or climate. Gradually, as choices are made, there are fewer variables. Decisions are replaced by affirmations, encouraging what thrives, and rooting out and forgetting the failures.

You are to be an English child, after all, and not a South African like your mother. You will come, a year old, to the area to which I came when I was one. Years later, when I was older and had a child to rear, I chose to return to it. To come back and live with the weeds and sounds of one's childhood is a very special way of returning to one's roots. Home is where the right weeds are, and I was afraid that if you spent any length of time in South Africa you would have always been an exile over here. Home is also where the right sounds are and I unwittingly returned to some of the sounds of my childhood when I bought this house: the sound of football play and applause, of steam trains, larks, church bells on Sundays if the wind is right and now, thanks to Harold, the crowing of a cock.

But what a difference time has made. I was a child in an exhilaratingly silent world and a cherished one. Bright colours in the hedges were wild flowers and not sweet wrappers. The sky still belonged almost entirely to the birds. Our world was bounded by our ability to walk and was reassuring in its attentiveness to young and old. There was little radio and no television to encourage people to despise their own neighbourhood.

The shopkeepers were our friends, not, as so often now, slaves

135

chained to electronic tills and conditioned by piped music. When Judith ran away at the age of six and walked down into the town a mile away it was the greengrocer who recognised her and phoned my mother to ask her if she knew her daughter was so far from home.

We lived in a small, warm, intimate world, and yet my mother instilled into me a maxim culled from I know not what philosophy: 'What would happen if everyone did that?' I found it very hard to live with, and as I grew up I envied those unburdened with such a yardstick.

Now I realise it is an essential one. We are discovering just what does happen if everyone does that. It is already happening. We are destroying our world – God's world – and with it ourselves and our neighbours. My neighbours are the trees and ants and swallows just as much as the people next door.

Since I started writing to you I have found in the charity shop a huge Victorian cash book with hard covers, red spine and glossy deckle-edged pages. It has become my common-place book and I have started copying into it a lifetime's collection of quotations, some of them dating from when I was a young student. One day it will be yours.

I wonder what you will make of it and which, out of all the items I have collected, will interest you and stay in your mind when you have read it.

Some of them are brief enough to make into wool texts:

'If fate hands you a lemon, make lemonade' (anonymous);

'The highest form of wisdom is kindness' (Jewish proverb);

'Love is the heart's own taste . . . it is the eye by which we can see God' (St Aelred);

'Every day is a messenger of God' (Russian proverb).

I like Schopenhauer on art: 'Treat a work of art as you would a prince – let it speak to you first.'

And on ideas: 'First they're ridiculous, then they're opposed, finally they're self-evident.'

Everyone should hear Edward Lear on education: 'I am almost thanking God I was never educated for it seems to me that 999 of those who are so, expensively and laboriously, have lost all before they arrive at my age and remain like Swift's Stullbruggs – cut and dry for life, making no use of their earlier gained treasures – whereas I seem to be on the threshold of knowledge.'

He was forty-seven when he wrote this. May you too, Daisy, be always on the threshold of knowledge.

My friends have all heard from me Dr Johnson's: 'It is worth seeing but it is not worth going to see.' It is an excuse for avoiding many journeys.

I only recently discovered Ben Franklin's pithy autobiography and in it his graphic illustration of how each of us tends to think we are right. Comparing the Quakers with other sects of his acquaintance he wrote:

> . . . every other sect supposing itself in possession of all truth, and that those who differ are so far in the wrong; like a man travelling in foggy weather, those at some distance before him on the road he sees wrapped up in the fog as well as those behind him, and also the people in the fields at each side, but near him all appears clear, though in truth he is as much in the fog as any of them.

I wish I had read Ben Franklin when I was young and able to benefit from his advice on the techniques of persuasion: how to convince other people by not being too dogmatic. I am afraid it is too late for me to start now.

I wish too, when I was young I had known the saying quoted

by Swift in a letter to Stella in 1712 about the relations between the sexes. Swift learned it from a great friend of his, Lady Orkney, née Elizabeth Villiers, once the mistress of William IV (and an amateur carpenter).

> Lady Orkney is making me a writing desk of her own contrivance and a bedgown,' he told Stella. 'She is perfectly kind, like a mother. The other day we had a long discourse with her about love: and she told us a saying of her sister Fitzharding which I thought excellent that in men desire begets love and in women love begets desire.

How that would explain the enchanting and maddening disparity between the sexes! What a pity Swift didn't report any more of that discourse.

Also in the commonplace book is the epitaph which Rahel wrote for herself in a letter when she was about sixty:

> Everything comes to my ears. I speak to all and all speak to me, every class. When I come to die, you may think 'she never was or pretended to be anything in herself; she only loved thought, and to make thought connected and harmonious; she understood Fichte, loved green fields, loved children; knew something of the arts, both of use and beauty: endeavoured to help God in his creatures always, uninterruptedly, and thanked God that he made her thus'.

Apart from the reference to Fichte, this would do for me. But I would prefer a briefer one: 'She tried to dance to the music of what happens, and she valued Lao Tse's three treasures of life, gentleness, economy and willingness not to be first.'

AFTERWORD

The lines on the rose quoted in Chapter Four come from Walter de la Mare's 'All That's Past'.

I am indebted to Helena Norbert-Hodge's *Ancient Futures* for the information about Ladakh in Chapter Three and to Julia Blackburn's *Charles Waterton* for the biographical information in Chapter Ten. Both books I recommend unreservedly. The Gerald Heard piece on St Francis de Sales in Chapter Eleven comes from *Saints for Now*, edited by Clare Boothe Luce.

Two footnotes to Chapter Two: Gilbert White may not have known where swallows went in the winter, but the Emperor Frederick II of Frankfurt did. In 1245 he wrote that they anticipated bad weather and departed for warmer climes. I was wrong about the disappearance of Milly-Molly-Mandy (who, incidentally, made her debut in the *Christian Science Monitor*). She returned as a Puffin in 1972.